1962
S0-AEG-732
3 0301 00019438 7

THE SCIENCES AND THE ARTS

Harper & Brothers, New York

the SCIENCES

and the ARTS

A New Alliance

by Harold Gomes Cassidy

Professor in Chemistry, Yale University

TO KATHRYN MYRA CHILDS CASSIDY

Who lives what I can only preach

THE SCIENCES AND THE ARTS

PRINTED IN THE UNITED STATES OF AMERICA

FIRST EDITION

A-M

LIBRARY OF CONGRESS CATALOG CARD NUMBER: 61-10236

Contents

"The end of our self-knowledge is not the contemplation by enlightened intellects of their own mysterious nature, but the freer and more effectual self-revelation of that nature in a vigorous practical life."

"What is wrong with us is precisely the detachment of these forms of experience—art, religion, and the rest—from one another; and our cure can only be their reunion in a complete and undivided life. Our task is to seek for that life, to build up the conception of an activity which is at once art, and religion, and science, and the rest."

R. G. Collingwood
Speculum Mentis,
Prologue, pp.
15 and 36.

Preface

In one variation of the Yale Arms, two elm trees interlace their branches behind a shield bearing the motto of the university. Symbolically, these interlaced trees could represent the living Arts and Sciences, flourishing under the shield of an Institution devoted to Light and Truth. To me that device represents the theme of this book.

This book is a personal testimony. It bears my answers to questions which became pressing when I undertook to construct a course in physical science for Yale College students who would not become scientists, but would enter other professions: government, law, business. In other words, for students "in the humanities." These questions clustered around the central one: Why should these people be required to study "science"? Does it provide something that they need which cannot be obtained in some other way? In what way (if at all) is it true that not to understand science today is to be culturally illiterate?

I have tested my answers to these questions by trying them out over the nation in lectures to, and discussions with, the most diverse kinds of audiences, from high school students to professional chemists, and I have found an answering concern in all parts of the country.

This has kept me at the heavy task of writing. It has been superimposed upon full-time teaching and research, and would hardly have been possible had I not received from the Fund for the Advancement of Education a Faculty Fellowship, which enabled me to get started; from Research Corporation, a Venture Grant; and from the National Institutes of Health, United States Public Health Service, grants which supported my graduate students and allowed teaching, research, and writing to proceed in harmony. I am happy to acknowledge all of these enabling gifts.

The subject of which I have written is controversial. In preparing to write upon it I have traveled far from the intellectual haunts in which I became at home as an organic chemist. Looking for guidance on the way, I have called on experts for their opinions, as indicated in the bibliography at the end of the book. Of course, if I quote some author with approbation it must not be construed that I subscribe to all else (or anything else) that he has said. My greatest assistance, however, has come from those friends who gave their time to reading and criticizing the numerous drafts of this manuscript. They are not, of course, committed in any way to the opinions in the book unless I explicitly say so. But it is a pleasure to thank them in print.

Dr. Wallace E. Childs, Madison, Indiana; Mr. and Mrs. Joseph E. Baird, of Panama Canal Zone; Professor Paul H. Carnell, Albion College; Professor John W. Chittum, Wooster College; Dean William C. DeVane, Professor and Mrs. Samuel B. Hemingway, Professor Charles W. Hendel, and Professor Henry Margenau, all of Yale University; Professor Howard Lee Nostrand, University of Washington; Mr. and Mrs. James A. Munro, Jr., Hamden, Connecticut; Professor Darnell Rucker, Colorado College; Dr. Henry C. Thacher, III, Argonne National Laboratory; Professor Charles A. Walker and Professor Alexander M. Witherspoon, Yale University, all read the manuscript at various stages from different points of view and strengthened it with constructive suggestions. I am particularly indebted to Mrs. Hemingway for her early, thoughtful evaluation of the work from the layman's point of view; to Professors Hendel, Margenau, and Rucker for technical criticism; and to Professor Witherspoon for a detailed examination of its presentation. I am indebted also to Mr. Elliot Offner for bringing Brancusi to my attention; and to

Dr. Orville F. Rogers for a room with a view.

My greatest debt is to Mr. Edward F. Haskell. Since our student days at Oberlin College we have been interested in problems of this type, and over the last ten years or so we have frequently discussed in detail his work on "Unified Science." At one stage of my manuscript he examined it with care and provided me with copious notes and suggestions. I have taken many of these. He has helped me to see connections more clearly and to clarify constructively the theme of this book. Throughout the text I have tried to indicate where important ideas originated with him. Though most of his work is as yet unpublished, he has generously permitted me to use freely what I have.

I am indebted to the following publishers and individuals for the use of materials cited by bibliographic reference:

American Scientist, Chap. 2, n. 23, and Figures 2 and 17; Beacon Press, Chap. 8, n. 14; Professor P. M. S. Blackett, Chap. 8, n. 17; *Bulletin of the Atomic Scientists,* Chap. 3, n. 3, and Chap. 8, n. 15; Chatto and Windus, Ltd., Chap. 3, n. 22; Clarendon Press, Oxford, Eng., Chap. 4, n. 8, Chap. 8, n. 8, and Figure 9; Columbia University Press, Chap. 9, n. 1, Chap. 9, nn. 1, 2 and 3; *Educational Forum,* Chap. 2, n. 20; French Reproduction Rights, Inc., Figures 13 and 14; George Allen and Unwin, Ltd., Chap. 5, n. 15; Harcourt, Brace & Co., Chap. 2, n. 22; Harper & Brothers, Chap. 8, n. 10, and Chap. 11, n. 7; *Harvard Educational Review,* Chap. 2, n. 19; W. Heffer & Sons, Ltd., Chap. 9, nn. 23, 27; *Industrial and Engineering Chemistry,* Chap. 5, n. 22; Johns Hopkins Press, Chap. 9, n. 13; *Journal of Chemical Education,* Chap. 5, n. 2; *Journal of Philosophy,* Chap. 6, n. 5; Alfred A. Knopf, Inc., Chap. 5, n. 8; Macmillan Company, Chap. 1, n. 2, and Chap. 4, n. 11; Macmillan & Co., Ltd., Chap. 7, n. 3; McGraw-Hill Book Co., Inc., Chap. 3, nn. 15, 16, 20, and Figures 3 and 6; Martinus Nijhoff, Figure 7; Methuen & Co., Ltd., Chap. 5, nn. 17, 19; Minton, Balch & Co., G. P. Putnam's Sons, Chap. 5, n. 21; Museum of Fine Arts, Boston, Figure 11; New American Library, Chap. 6, n. 3; Mr. Ernest Newman, Chap. 4, n. 12; *New York Times,* Chap. 5, n. 18, and Chap. 9, n. 14; Philadelphia Museum of Art, Figures 15 and 16; Presbyterian and Reformed Publishing Co., Chap. 9, n. 6; Princeton University Press, Chap. 4, nn. 2, 4, and Chap. 8, n. 11; Routledge and Kegan Paul, Ltd., Chap. 8, n. 9; *Saturday Review,* Chap. 11, n. 3; *Science,* Chap. 3, n. 4, Chap. 8, nn. 12, 13, 16, and Chap. 9, n. 18; Science Press, Chap. 4, n. 19; Scripta Mathematica, Chap. 2, n. 12; Sir C. P. Snow, Chap. 9, n. 4; University of Chicago Press, Chap. 7, n. 4; University of North Carolina Press, Chap. 2, nn. 15, 16, 17, 21, and Chap. 3, nn. 11, 12, 14, 21, and 22; A. Watkins, Inc., Chap. 8, nn. 4, 5; John Wiley & Sons, Inc., Chap. 5, n. 10; Professor Roger J. Williams, Figure 18; Wittenborn, Schultz, Inc., Chap. 3, n. 17, Chap. 4, nn. 6, 7, and Chap. 7, n. 2; Yale University Press, Chap. 4, nn. 13, 15, Chap. 8, n. 18, Chap. 9, n. 8, and Figure 12.

I am also indebted to Miss Patricia A. Bracken, who typed several revisions of the manuscript; to Miss Helen M. Goebel, who typed one of them, and to Mrs. Mildred R. Bray, who typed the final one.

How does one acknowledge the manifold subtle contributions of his wife? Perhaps I have moved a little way in this direction by dedicating the book to her.

HAROLD GOMES CASSIDY

BOLINAS
BERKELEY COLLEGE
PEMASONG

CHAPTER 1

Introduction

To write of the sciences and the arts is to write of matters that touch almost every aspect of life. In particular, if we try to compare these two areas of experience to see in what important ways they differ and how they differ inconsequentially or not at all, we find the entire spectrum of experience—from imaginative poetry and art through common sense experience to imaginative physics and cosmology—included in our scheme.

All the practical things that we do or that we experience have been influenced by efforts that may be classed as humanistic (the arts) or scientific. We live in a web of connectedness with the world. We are connected not only to events that are close to us, events related to our families, homes, and jobs, but to events that are far away in space—on the other side of the world and in the sun—and far away in time—the actions of our ancestors and the thoughts, visions, and actions of countless earlier inhabitants of this world. We are enmeshed in this nexus with the world, and yet in many ways we seem alone. For how can we impart, even to our closest love, those feelings for which there are no words, those states for which the word "ineffable" was coined? Still, some inner urge drives us to try, by whatever means we have or can devise or can discover, to link our thoughts and emotions—our experiences—with those of others; to mitigate our sense of appalling uniqueness. And the results of these efforts at communication are also classed among the humanities or the sciences and comprise some of mankind's greatest achievements.

This book, which is about these efforts at communication, has a two-fold purpose: first, to compare and describe some aspects of the sciences and the arts (humanities); and second, to offer prescriptions for the cure of some present cultural ills by examining the causes of the common misunderstanding between scientists and humanists. I hope to lessen that misunderstanding, to desensitize those scientists and artists who, fixing upon one position, are allergic to the other. For, while an underlying theme of this book is, in Paul Curie's phrase, that "it is dyssymmetry that creates phenomena," it is my thesis that the sciences and the arts, though different in many ways, are not mutually exclusive or fundamentally contradictory. They are complementary parts of our culture; loss or injury to one is damage to the other and to the whole; and neither the scientist nor the humanist need fear to respect the other. In fact, in their mutual understanding lie the possibilities of unimagined cultural advances.

One source of their current, mutual misunderstanding is the common attitude that science is simply an instrument for making traditional humanism more effective: "science has implemented the humanism which classicism and Christianity have proclaimed."[1] This attitude is based upon an incomplete knowledge or a misunderstanding of the nature of science, which arises when the analytical and descriptive parts of science, or the technological parts, are taken for the whole. It is a dangerous attitude because it is incorrect. The fact is that science is no passive instrument of humanism. Science is changing our culture in ways beyond the ken of a person who knows no science. Science can be an instrument only of that humanist who understands science, and in the process of getting understanding the humanist will be changed. In this connection I recall the strong words of the historian H. Butterfield. Writing of the scientific revolution, the roots of which reach well back before the sixteenth century, he says:

> Since that revolution overturned the authority in science not only of the middle ages but of the ancient world—since it ended not only in the eclipse of scholastic philos-

> ophy but in the destruction of Aristotelian physics—it outshines everything since the rise of Christianity, and reduces the Renaissance and Reformation to the rank of mere episodes, mere internal displacements, within the system of medieval Christendom. Since it changed the character of men's habitual mental operations, even in the conduct of the non-material sciences, while transforming the whole diagram of the physical universe and the very texture of human life itself, it looms so large as the real origin both of the modern world and of the modern mentality that our customary periodisation of European history has become an anachronism and an incumbrance.[2]

Science is no instrument of humanism; but both, functioning together, form a powerful instrument for understanding the world.

A balanced response to science and art can come only from people who do not fear science, but understand its power and its limitations—people who have such faith in the ultimate power of truth, wherever it may be found, that they are not afraid to look for it; people who believe that what is true in art or science remains true always, even though it may be continually reinterpreted.

This book is directed toward the evocation of such a balanced response. Articulate artists and humanists who understand science can, with the aid of scientists who understand them, direct and control the forces of cultural change, practically and justly.[3] And a real union of the sciences and the arts can enable men to agree on what is practical, moral, and just.

The following chapter (Chapter 2) is devoted to an examination of two works, one by an artist, the other by a scientist, providing, so to speak, two pieces of raw data. These enable us to view some of the problems to be treated more completely later after certain important terms are defined. Chapter 3 analyzes the data used by scientists and artists to see whether there is a clear-cut difference, marking certain kinds of experience exclusively for the scientist and others solely for the use of the artist. The next three chapters examine the methods of scientist and artist

(Chapter 4) and the kinds of results that they achieve by applying these methods (Chapters 5 and 6). Chapters 7 and 8 are devoted to examining certain general problems which confront us all, namely, problems having to do with relativeness and the function of absolutes and problems of value. Chapter 9 indicates, even though briefly and inadequately, some of the ways in which artists and scientists can improve their understanding of each other. Chapter 10 is a prescription, based on the diagnosis which arises out of the first eight chapters, for healing the schism between the sciences and the humanities. The last chapter (Chapter 11) is a summary and exhortation.

CHAPTER 2

Art and Science

Men who seek to understand the world go about their search in many different ways. Some are drawn to contemplation. This is a difficult path at best; and in the modern world—even in the Orient—its difficulty is increased by a prevailing attitude that action is what is valuable. Thus, whereas once a man might have said "understanding is for the purposes of contemplation," now he is led to say "understanding is for the purposes of control." Yet the two are not mutually exclusive reasons for seeking understanding.

Men who seek understanding may be classified by their activities: artists, scientists, technologists, managers, and so on. I call a man an artist if he produces works of art; a scientist if he produces works of science; a craftsman or technician if he makes or does things skillfully, but with circumscribed vision; a technologist if in practice he creatively executes the general principles of art or science; a manager if he manipulates the products of artist, scientist, or others for known purposes. All these are the classifications of logic; they shade one into the other; and a particular man may in fact, on the basis of his work, belong in more than one category.

Now, it is frequently easier to deal with complicated matters by subdividing them into parts and examining the parts one or two at a time. Yet as we wrench each part from its context we may distort it. Sometimes it is easier to avoid distortion by dealing with extreme examples than with borderline cases. Thus, physics is clearly a science, and poetry is clearly one of the arts. But it is difficult to decide how to classify mathematics, "one of the most modern of sciences and, at the same time, one of the most ancient of the humanities,"[1] or where to house history, that uneasy tenant who wanders from place to place, never sure whether his landlord is the dean of the social sciences or the humanities.

Let us begin our examination of science and art, then, by looking at the extremes, physics and poetry. I have chosen for comparison a few lines from a longer poem, and a formula taken out of a longer work by a physicist. These concrete examples will serve as points of departure for initial comparisons and will show the need for certain basic definitions. Although I have chosen a poem because it is easy to reproduce here, much that I shall say about it in contrasting it with the formula will be applicable to other kinds of art—to literature in general, music, painting, and so on. And what I say about the physics formula might apply equally well to suitable statements from chemistry, biology, geology, astronomy, psychology, or any other science.

A variety of opinion exists about the relation between art and science. However careful we may be in approaching the subject, the problem is so complex, we cannot single out one approach as the best and only one without landing in an embarrassing morass. Even in the less emotionally charged areas of physical science there is no royal road to interpretation. But some approaches seem more reasonable than others.

Here, then, are two works, one of art, one of science:

The Poet	*The Scientist*
When to the new eyes of thee All things by immortal power Near or far, Hiddenly To each other linked are That thou canst not stir a flower Without troubling of a star;	$\mathbf{F}_{\text{gravit.}} \propto \frac{m_1\, m_2}{s^2}$

One was wrought by the poet Francis Thompson,[2] and the other by Sir Isaac Newton.[3] Both deal with majestic ideas that comprehend the whole universe; both reach from the earth to the stars. Both have the function of communication between the author and his reader. But the ideas they communicate, the purposes to which the two works are directed—their "end uses"—are different; and the language in which they are couched, and even their appearances, are different. Yet, surely both speak about the same universe and thereby are connected. Both are products of the human mind engaged in creative activity. And they must be related in many other ways. Our concern is with the connections and similarities as well as with the authentic differences between them.

At first reading, what the poet says is clear. He writes English. He uses words and a grammar that we have been brought up from childhood to understand. But unless one is familiar with its nomenclature the scientific statement must be explained. It says that the gravitational force, ($\mathbf{F}_{\text{gravit.}}$) between two bodies (designated by the subscripts 1 and 2) is proportional ($\propto$) to the product of their masses (m_1m_2) divided by the square of the distance (s^2) between their centers of gravity. It is common in physics to use $\mathbf{F}$ to symbolize a force; *m*, a mass; and *s*, a distance. But this proportionality is approximated only if the diameters of the two bodies of mass 1 and mass 2 are small relative to the distance *s*. The nature of the bodies is not specified, and since the diameters of, say, an earthly flower and a star are small relative to the distance between them, this formula would hold for the case of the poet's flower and star. It states that a gravitational link connects them. When the diameters of the two objects are not small relative to the distance between them, another formula, more suited to the physical situation, must be used. But in every case, any two bodies exert a gravitational attraction upon each other, and by such forces all material things are linked.

Once, after I had spoken on this subject to a group of university teachers, one said that in using these two examples I had "stacked the cards". As he put it, *anyone* could understand the verse, but *hardly anyone* the formula. He added that I should have used either a more subtly stated poem or a simpler formula, so as to "keep the competition even." This attitude is, of course, symptomatic of the breach between scientist and artist which we seek to heal—I see no question of competition. I might, of course, have chosen a poem with such subtle and obscure imagery that it would have needed explication for all but *aficionados*. But I might also have chosen a more complicated formula. The examples I am using make the distinctions simpler and sharper. However, at the end of this chapter, and for another reason, I shall examine a poem with subtle and hidden imagery.

Both statements are concerned with an imaginative idea. But the scientific statement, compact and general, is couched in spare language. The poetic is also compact and general in its own way—it starts with a general statement, then sharpens it into a particular case—but it is couched in evocative language. The scientific formula is quantitative; the poem is a model of qualitative precision. The quantitative precision of the formula is obtained by the use of symbols which, intentionally, are as purely denotative as possible. They refer strictly to quantities the measurement of which has been specified by scientific conventions; they indicate the relations between those quantities. By their connotative barrenness, their mathematical nakedness, they achieve the quantitative precision and generality which is an aim of every scientific law. They have the ability to convey as nearly as is possible exactly the same meaning to different people irrespective of differences in cultural background or language —exactly, that is, when functioning as a scientific statement. The poem, on the other hand, because of its connotational richness, evokes different responses in different people even though there may be no language barrier and they may belong to the same nation.

For example, the words "stars" and "flowers" may denote, and certainly do connote, different things, emotions, and ideas to a Midwestern farmer than they do to a dweller in Manhattan's canyons. And they mean something still different to a person from the Lone-Star State. On the other hand, such concepts as force, mass, and distance mean exactly the same thing to every physicist when he is using them as scientific concepts. Of course, the physicist is a human being too, and so "force" has all sorts of nonscientific connotations to him, but he has trained himself to exclude these from the **F** in his scientific formula. Nothing but lack of talent prevents him from writing a poem or composing music about the other "forces." But the formula and related mathematical expressions are the only "poems" he can write about his connotationally naked **F**.

In explaining the formula I converted it into a wordy sentence with exactly the same meaning. This was not a translation in the ordinary sense. A foreign reader who knows no English would have to have the scientific terms translated into his language, just as the poem would have to be translated for him. But the poem would lose something in the translation, while the formula and its equivalent sentence would not be appreciably affected. This is why scientific works, communicated in the spare, denotational language of our formula, are cosmopolitan, while poetry (particularly poetry, of all works of art) is provincial. This is why science is international while art—particularly the poetry and songs of a nation—creates and supports national character.[4]

The poem and the formula are directed to different ends. That is, they are directed to different *immediate* ends (their ultimate end is to tell us something about the world). But before we can say what the immediate ends are, we must examine what it is that the work of art and the work of science communicate and how the terms "knowledge," "truth," and "meaning" apply to their messages.

When I speak of "art" I mean the activity of the artist as we observe him at work, as his activity becomes manifest in the work of art, and as he tells us what he is doing and how he is doing it (though many critics discount the artist's own report). The work of art itself is also often called "art," and I may slip into this usage for convenience when no serious confusion can result. But I shall use the term "art" primarily as a generalization from the activities of the painter, poet, musician, and so forth. Then, "the arts" is an academic term for the named disciplines, each usually housed in a named academic department, in which painting, writing, musical composition, and so on, are taught and criticized.

Analogously, "science" is a term generalized from the activity of scientists as we observe them, from the results they obtain, and from what they are doing and how. Scientists, like artists, are usually specialists; so we have physics, chemistry, biology, psychology, and so forth. There are as many scientific activities as there are scientists, and it is from all these activities that I generalize to "science." "The sciences" is a term for all the disciplines (conveniently found, like "the arts," by reference to a college catalog) which study and teach science as it is applied to the special data of physics, chemistry, and so on.

My definitions of "the sciences" and "the arts" (or "arts and letters," or "the humanities") are good because they can be checked by anyone who has access to the catalog of a large college or university and because they are based on well-recognized phenomena—the various disciplines that are embodied in college and university departments of instruction. There is some overlapping between these groups, and many of them shelter subdivisions to which I shall pay no attention, since their position will be obvious, e.g., biochemistry, geophysics. If I arrange into groups ("physical sciences," "behavioral sciences") the disciplines I have selected, and place them in a circle as shown in Figure 1, I can define the arts and the sciences as comprising the halves of a circle. The arrangement is a formal one, which for my purposes has advantages over a mere alphabetical listing of the disciplines (as appears in most catalogs). It is a useful device for providing the best definitions for "the arts" and "the sciences" that I can find.

One of the advantages of the arrangement is that it suggests a connectedness among the disciplines. For example, there is a progression in the sequence, physics, chemistry, biology, social science (I have used the term "physical sciences" for the first two, and equally general terms for the others) if one considers the increasing complexity of the phenomena studied through these disciplines. The complexity may show itself in terms of the increasing difficulty of isolating variables, or in the increasing preoccupation with phenomena which depend on the behavior of small groups of individuals, and so on. Again, mathematics, logic, language, literature, and "art" all seem to be connected. If one looks at the ways in which discourse is conceptualized there certainly seems to be a concatenation.

Some may feel that a schematization of this kind does violence to individual areas of experience. But such a feeling rests on too literal an interpretation of the scheme. I do not mean to

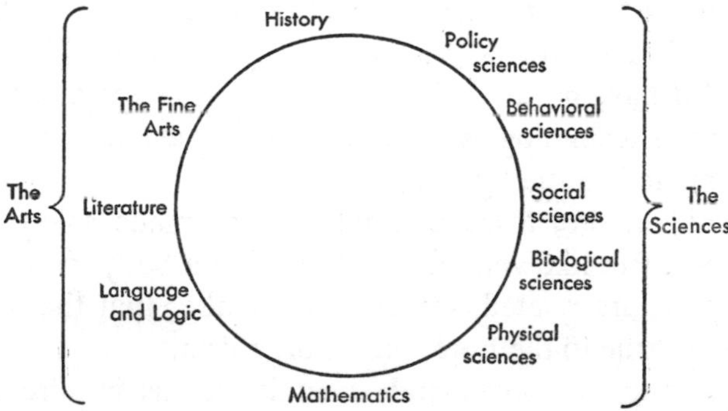

Figure 1. Definition of the sciences and the arts. See accompanying text for interpretation of the figure.

imply that mathematics and physics are connected in the same way as are mathematics and modern logic. Nor does the placement of the physical sciences opposite the fine arts imply that they are truly opposite kinds of activities. The various disciplines are arranged at the distances from each other shown in the figure only for typographical convenience. The only implication of the figure, apart from a suggestion or relative order among the disciplines, is that the *field* of knowledge and experience comprising the arts and sciences is a continuum; all of that knowledge and experience is interrelated. This important fact is explicitly symbolized by Figure 1.

I visualize the arts and the sciences as abstractions from

that single field—abstractions which have all these characteristics that people generally associate with the arts and the sciences. Now, since much current talk and writing alludes to them as opposites, it is descriptive to set up a contrast between them. Of course, this academic "pie" might be sliced in many ways besides the even division I have chosen. Some people might prefer three slices: the sciences, the liberal arts (or humanities), and the social sciences (or "humanistic sciences," as they have infelicitously been called).[5] I find it easier to contrast two groups than three, one of which has the properties of a chameleon. Others might separate the so-called "interpretive humanities," comprising history and criticism, from the rest, the "creative humanities."[6] I shall make this distinction in a different way. (Although I have not included in Figure 1 theology, philosophy, ethics, or the technologies, I shall show in a later context how they are related to the figure.)

As I said before, these distinctions are made solely for our convenience. But like anatomists dissecting a body to see how its smallest parts are related, we must remember that the separated parts are not true to the functioning organism.

Returning to our poem and formula, let us inquire whether it is knowledge that poet and scientist communicate. More generally, is communication of knowledge a primary function of the artist and the scientist? The answer I should like to give is, "yes," for the scientist, "no," for the artist; it is a primary function of the scientist to contribute to the body of knowledge, whereas it is *not* a primary function of the artist, though he may, incidentally, do so.

It might be objected that this answer depends on my defining "knowledge" in a way which does not seem to fit general usage. But the term is commonly used in so many different ways that I must narrow my definition of it in order to deal with the important distinction between science and art that I wish to bring out. I hestitate to abandon the term and adopt some other instead, because "knowledge" has useful connotations. It applies to a state which is inferior to that of understanding; we commonly assume that ony may have knowledge without understanding. For the purposes of exposition, then, I shall adopt the definition used by the philosopher Bertrand Russell[7] and define "knowledge" as true beliefs based on sound reasons (not on lucky guesses) and displayed in statements.

By this definition, knowledge, since it relies upon statements, can be communicated between people only through linguistic means, that is, through signs and symbols than can be spoken or written in a discursive way and for which there is a recognized grammar and syntax. These include the signs and symbols of logic, mathematics, and geometry. There is, of course, a great deal that can be communicated by nonverbal means—as in painting, sculpture, music, dance, and some rituals—but by my definition, what is communicated in those ways is not knowledge. Although we frequently use "knowledge" to apply to some of these nonlinguistic commnications, I shall here restrict the term to the definition and provide other ways of dealing with other kinds of communication. For example, I shall not class as knowledge what is communicated in a ballet, even though there is a kind of grammar, "the ballet way of saying things," and a kind of syntax in the dance. Nor would I class what is communicated by music as knowledge, even though the notes are strung out along a strand of time and certain musical phrases have come to be closely associated with a theme or message. There are philosophers who say that propositions can be expressed in other media than words. But it seems to me that it is more reasonable to take the position that in so far as there is no agreed convention to connect sounds, colors, shapes, and so on, with definite things, relations, or concepts, these cannot assert anything at all. I would then say that conveyance of knowledge is not the primary concern of the nonlinguistic arts. Obviously, my definition is arbitrary, but in restricting the term I do not violate good usage. Perhaps for the very reason that it is arbitrary it is more useful to us; it is a sort of conceptual scalpel which dissects from a single living body of knowledge and experience a part for closer examination.

Of course, one can have knowledge in the restricted sense *about* painting, music, the dance, and so forth; and artists and critics (often the same person) may contribute to this part of the body of knowledge. Indeed, a good deal of the activity of teachers in the arts is directed to developing and transmitting knowledge of this kind. But the artist is not, in the same sense as the scientist, *primarily* concerned with developing and communicating knowledge through the work of art. If he conveys knowledge, it comes as a bonus.

Now, it is plain that the scientific equation does convey knowledge. The equation uses applied mathematics to generalize a host of empirical observations into a form which has been called a categorical proposition. The statement asserts that a relationship exists among $\mathbf{F}, m_1$, m_2, and s (when these are measured in specified ways and when the value of s is large compared with the diameters of m_1 and m_2). It is empirically true because what it asserts has been found to accord with empirically observed facts: when $\mathbf{F}$, m_1, m_2, and s are measured in consistent units for many different systems, the values found fulfill the stated relation.

I chose for my illustration the statement of a scientific law. I might also (but less effectively) have used a simple analytic statement of fact, such as that the earth and the moon exert a gravitational attraction for each other. This would be a special case of the law if it were stated in terms of the actual masses of the earth and moon and of the force and distance between them. Most of the results of science consist of such particular statements of fact. These statements vary in quantitativeness. For example, the statement that at 25 degrees centigrade water has a relative density of 0.99707 grams per milliliter is quantitative, while the statement that milk sugar is not as sweet as cane sugar is not quantitative. Another kind of scientific statement gathers together, or generalizes, smaller or larger groups of particular statements: these are the hypotheses and theories. Finally, there are the statements which generalize a tremendous number of particular statements: these are the fundamental laws, such as Newton's laws, Einstein's laws, the laws of thermodynamics, and so on. All of these constitute knowledge.

There are scientific works, however, which cannot be said to convey knowledge. These are the actual experimental procedures: the mixing of reagents to produce new compounds, the crossing of organisms to produce hybrids, the observation of a satellite, the analysis of a mineral, the study of the reactions of a rat to various stimuli. These are perhaps more closely analogous to the work of art, since they are particular works rather than statements. I distinguish them from works of art for reasons which will become apparent as we proceed. One reason is that scientists have invented methods for converting particular works into symbolic forms: equations, diagrams, charts. These do convey knowledge, and constitute what I mean by scientific results, or work. The artist cannot convert, or translate, his works in the same way; it is the critic and art teacher who may make the conversion.

Whether or not a poem conveys knowledge is not so plain. According to my definition, music, painting, sculpture, and so forth, do not convey knowledge since they are not expressed linguistically. But the poem, and literature in general, are expressed in language. In his poem Francis Thompson does convey knowledge. Very likely his inspiration drew upon his knowledge of natural science, for educated people of his day had studied natural science in school, and many continued their interest after graduation. Thompson himself had studied medicine for a time. But to convey knowledge about natural science is not the primary purpose of the poem. Thompson felt that there is a deep, mystical connection among all the things in the universe; and it is this insight, or dream, or hope, that the poem conveys, rather than a specific knowledge of gravitation.

This point was made clear to me in the course of the lecture I mentioned earlier. The comment had been made by one of the audience that *hardly anyone* could understand the formula while *anyone* could understand the poem. I therefore tried to bring home to the audience the meaning of the formula. Pointing to two men sitting side by side in the front row, I said "m_1 and m_2

might refer to the masses of you two gentlemen. These are related to your weights. And *s* refers to the distance between your centers of gravity. We would have to use a different formula in this case because the distance between you is of the same general magnitude as the breadth and length of your bodies but, nonetheless, the principle remains the same, and we could calculate an **F** which is the gravitational attraction between the two of you." I was, in fact, carried away by the picture of a web of gravitational connections linking the audience—a fact they were learning effectively for the first time. "Isn't it fascinating," I continued, "to contemplate that you two men, and indeed all of us in this room, are linked (even though weakly, it is true) by this nexus of gravitational forces?" Whereupon one of the men, with a look of distaste on his face, burst out: "I find it positively repulsive!" Yet he had not found Thompson's poem repulsive, even though it said just this. Clearly, then, the poem conveyed no knowledge to him. And equally clearly, it, too, required explication.

Since literature may embody true statements, it may, of course, convey knowledge. But this is not its primary purpose as literature.

To clarify what I mean, let us examine the way the arts and the sciences are taught in the colleges. In a department of music or literature or chemistry there is a great deal that is taught by verbal means, which if true, we class as knowledge. But there is also a great deal that is communicated nondiscursively—through listening to musical compositions, viewing paintings, sculptures, or dances, and doing certain kinds of laboratory work—which I class not as knowledge but as "experience." Experience is that "immediate acquaintance with" things that many philosophers distinguish from knowledge. "The one is knowledge about things, the other is immediate acquaintance with them; the one is given *par excellence* by science, the other by art."[8] The teaching of any discipline includes exposing the student to direct experiences as well as conveying knowledge about them. Often, the two are inextricably united—even effectively indistinguishable. One of the differences between the way the arts (the humanities) and the sciences are taught is that a course in the arts emphasizes communicable content that we would not call knowledge (compositions, paintings, and so forth) supplemented by knowledge about it, while a course in the sciences emphasizes discursively communicable content, supplemented by the nonverbal experience of demonstration and laboratory work.

Of course, examining the way these subjects are taught can also show the marked similarities in function between scientists and humanists. In aesthetics, art criticism, history of art, and philosophy of art, a large body of knowledge is imparted, as well as in literary criticism, and all the other areas of criticism and philosophy in the humanities. In such courses, the works of art (novels, plays, poetry) are, like scientific data, not primarily communications of knowledge, but rather the data about which knowledge is communicated. Here the art teacher (and in general, the teacher in the humanities) acts like the science teacher.

Again we see that the laboratory experiment bears some resemblance to the work of art. Professor Herbert Harned[9] once said to me, during a discussion of research in chemistry, that instruction in research is a lot like the best instruction in music. You can talk about it. But then the neophyte has to go off by himself and practice. After a while he comes back and rehearses what he has done. Then the experienced teacher listens, finds flaws, exposes artlessness, approves creative insights, suggests subtler interpretations, and so helps the student to grow and become educated.

Even though it is sometimes difficult to separate them, it is, nevertheless, useful to distinguish "knowledge" from "experience." The philosopher Professor Susanne K. Langer has used the term "discursive symbolism" to distinguish language proper from other means of communication.[10] Music, art, dance utilize what she terms "presentational symbolism." Some philosophers have objected to Professor Langer's use of the word "symbolism" in this phrase, and I shall avoid it. But I shall speak of experience as communicated by presentational means, including musical notes, color, form, texture in painting, and so on.

I defined knowledge as true beliefs that are displayed in statements. The term "beliefs" is sufficiently defined in the simple phrase of Dean W. R. Matthews: we really believe that which we are normally prepared to act upon.[11] "Truth," however, is not so clearly defined. What do we mean when we say that our equation and our poem communicate truth?

In one aspect "truth" is primarily a logical term. It is a property of statements. A proposition "*x* implies *y*" is true if *x* does indeed imply *y* when the test of deducing *y* from *x* is made—that is, when *x* implies *y* by logical necessity. In any such statement, it is the form of the statement that is true. This is the kind of truth one finds in mathematics. It is called *formal truth*. As an example, I might say: "If every *a* is a *b*, and every *b* is a *c*, then every *a* is a *c*." This is equivalent to saying, "Every *a* is a *b*, and every *b* is a *c* imply that every *a* is a *c*." Here, if I wished, I could replace the first eleven words up to *imply* by *x*, and the last six by *y*, and obtain "*x* implies *y*." The formal truth of this statement holds by logical necessity independently of any content that might be introduced by replacing *a*, *b*, and *c* by definite words. Such statements are called hypothetical propositions. They are statements about the logically possible. I refer to this for a reason that will become apparent when I discuss the nature of physical reality.

Science deals with the actual world. In science, deductive consequences of scientific statements are empirically true if they are borne out by observable fact; then they qualify as scientific knowledge. This relation between mathematics and science is nicely stated by Professor C. J. Keyser, when he says that the combined scope of mathematics and science "is the twofold world of the Actual and the logically Possible." Scientific truth about the actual world, the world of propositional fact, is discoverable "by none but empirical thinking, wherein Observation is sovereign." Truth in the world of the logically possible, the world of propositional form "is discoverable by none but postulational thinking, wherein Deduction is sovereign."[12]

Philosophers through the years have been aware of the distinction between the logically possible and the actual, and many famous controversies have centered on the question of which is to be preferred. Both have their place in man's search for knowledge and understanding. Even if man knew all the facts there were about the actual world there would still be the world of the logically possible for him to investigate. But whenever the logically possible can be tested against facts, the latter decide for the scientist. However, when empirical truth is lacking, the logically possible is invoked as a guide in the search for further knowledge. The kind of truth communicated by our scientific formula is empirical truth: it accords with repeatedly observed facts.

Turning to the poem, I find that the truth it conveys is not scientific truth, but a kind of truth peculiar to the arts. "Truth," like "knowledge," is one of those words which is used in different senses. Semanticists call such words "multiordinal": the meaning of the word changes with the context in which it is used.[13] Fortunately, the problem of the meaning of "truth" has been dealt with in a felicitous way by John Hospers.[14] He designates scientific truth as "truth-*about*" the subject matter, and artistic truth as "truth-*to*" the subject matter (but not in such meanings of true-to as that a photograph is true-to the original, or a man is true-to his word).

What I mean by "true-to" is not that there is a perfect correspondence between the work of art and some observable original, but that the work of art reveals something universal; I may say that it is in a sense "more true than life itself." The concept is, of course, a complicated one. I do not mean that art deals with types. In literature (or poetry) the characters must be "true-to human nature," not, or only incidentally, true-to particular people who have actually lived.

> Becky Sharp never existed in the flesh, yet the world is full of Becky Sharps, and probably Thackeray's heroine

> is a truer, more convincing picture of Becky Sharps everywhere than any of the particular historical members of the class ever have been or will be.[15]

The same considerations apply to events and to actions. An important point is that the "truth-to" of literature is not verifiable in the empirical, scientific sense. Yet it is "true-to human nature as we know it. Thus in a way we *can* verify what the artist has presented; we can verify his insights in our own further observations of people and actions"[16] and in the response to it from our own experience.

Poetry, literature, painting, and art in general can be true-to much else beside human character and action. For example, it can be said that true art is true-to "the felt qualities of experience in general."[17] The artist may use his medium evocatively for the communication of a heightened consciousness, an increased sensibility towards what things "really look like."

I could continue at length with examples, but perhaps enough has been said to show a real difference between scientific truth and artistic truth. In the sense of "true-to," our illustrative poem is true in that it communicates a dream, an intuition, a hope, perhaps, which we feel in contemplating the unity of nature. It is true-to the human heart and to the felt qualities of experience. This is its poetic justification.

I have said that our poem and formula communicate truths of universal import. This is not a characteristic of all works of art and science—far from it. There is in each area a gamut of qualities, reaching from the trivial to the most significant—from work requiring skill alone to work requiring skill, knowledge, insight, and vision all together. The former I would call works of craft or technique; the latter, works of art and science. There is no signpost along this way which says for all to see "this side art" or "this side craft." The extremes are in clear enough contrast: on one side bric-a-brac and "pot-boiling" experiments, possibly skillfully executed but superficial and without a large purpose; on the other, the highest, most subtle, comprehensive, lucid, finely conceived and executed works that mankind has achieved. But along the way, where one type shades into the other, the fuzziness of our logical distinctions becomes apparent. A work may partake of both qualities in different ways, and there is plenty of room for differences of opinion and for clarifying discussion. (There is room for discussion all along the line, of course, but the closer one gets to the extremes the less room there is for maneuvering.) The problem of classifying a work is familiar under various names, and I shall return to it in the last chapter.

I should like now to define three more logical classes, which will help us in later chapters to understand some of the modern movements in the fields of the arts, sciences, and philosophy and to make distinctions between craft and art works, technique and scientific works.

The activities described earlier may be classified into three types: analytic, synthetic, and reduction to practice. Every man, whatever his vocation—whether he be artist, scientist, or technologist—is engaged in these activities. Every discipline or profession includes, apart from teaching, at least these three related and overlapping kinds of functions.

The analytic activity involves accumulating data: increasing specific knowledge or particular experience. It is analytic in the sense that it involves making distinctions, dividing, classifiying. In both arts and sciences it includes making collections, naming, observing, and reporting observations in detail. The chemist performs this function when he distinguishes among different substances, among ores of different kinds, for example, and when he determines the composition of materials. The biologist performs it when he classifies animals or plants into families, genera, and species, and names them. The critic performs it when he classifies paintings, for example, in terms of techniques used (water color, oil, fresco, tempera), or when he dissects a musical composition, as in the method of stylometric analysis. Analogous analytic activity, ranging from the obvious to the subtle, supports the distinctions that divide one profession or one academic department from another in the arts as well as in the sciences.

The second kind of activity, the synthetic, occurs when connections are sought among data, among theories, and among theories of theories[18]—when trends, hypotheses, theories, and laws are derived. One synthesis may bring together other lesser syntheses. For example, the theory of relativity includes within itself, as a special case, Newtonian physics. Evolution theory contains within itself, among others, theories of speciation, which in turn include theories of genetics and ecology. Beethoven's *Ninth Symphony* includes within itself a fugue, a type of composition characteristic of an earlier school. Synthetic activity can be further subdivided into deductive and inductive. When a critic, after examining innumerable art works, proposes a theory of the development or evolution of a style, or when, analogously, a scientist synthesizes quantities of data into a rule or a law, the synthetic activity may chiefly involve the logical unfolding of relationships, or deduction. On the other hand, when, through a creative act, the artist or scientist produces something new—something not previously discoverable by logical means, an invention, a creation as unpredictable as a flash of inspiration—the synthetic activity is primarily inductive. The result of inductive synthesis on the part of the artist may be a masterpiece of music, painting, or writing; on the part of the scientist, it may be the invention of a great synthesizing theory, like the theory of evolution, or of a law, like the law of gravitation, or, in a smaller way, of an object, like a new drug specific against some disease. In practice, both kinds of synthetic activity operate together, and the distinction between them is generally maintained. I am much more interested in being able to distinguish synthetic from analytic activities.

The analytic and the synthetic shade into each other, and often it is difficult to decide which is being demonstrated in a given instance. In such cases the distinction is usually unnecessary. The two functions are compatible and necessary to each other. Nevertheless, they are sometimes contrasted. One author says, for example, "experience has taught us that as between synthesis, with its risk of misplaced abstractedness, generality, and loss of specificity; and division, with its risk of compartmentalization, division is to be preferred. For among distinctions made, it is always possible to recognize unities and similarities; among distinctions erased, it is not always possible to recognize important differences.[19] But experience has also taught us that a preference for division rather than synthesis is likely to imply a preference for disintegrative, fragmentizing activities. The statement is comparable to preferring one wing of a plane to another; but experience has taught that it takes *both* wings, functioning together, to fly.

Failure to distinguish between analytic and synthetic functions, accompanied, often, by a "preference" for one or the other, is one of the chief causes of schism between scientists and humanists. For example, a book on educational philosophy published in 1957 implies the common belief that science has been entirely analytic. The author says in the Preface, "it [the prime objective of education, which is preservation of social continuity] is made even more difficult *now that modern science is no longer merely a report of particular facts . . .*"(my italics).[20] This is an example of the common error of considering a part of science (analysis) to be all of science. I wish especially to emphasize that *analytic science and art is only partial science and art.*

The third kind of activity which art and science include is reduction to practice: the activity which returns from the general or theoretical to the particular or practical, the activity which puts to use on a particular occasion the general or theoretical. Ultimately, knowledge and experience are sought for use and have a use, and it is in their application, their reduction to practice, that the results of analytic and synthetic activties are tested for validity. All three activities—analysis, synthesis, and reduction to practice—must go together for science or art to be healthy.

This classification of activities is intimately connected to the definitions of the arts and sciences discussed earlier in this chapter in connection with Figure 1. In that discussion I noted that there are certain disciplines of which I did not take account in my definitions. By utilizing the classification of activities I can now relate to each other all the disciplines by means of another figure (Figure 2). In this figure I diagram four divisions of the continuum of knowledge and experience, as they are exemplified in a university. Near the top of the diagram synthesis is emphasized; near the bottom, reduction to practice.

The more theoretical departments and professions lean to the analytic and synthetic functions, while the technologies emphsize

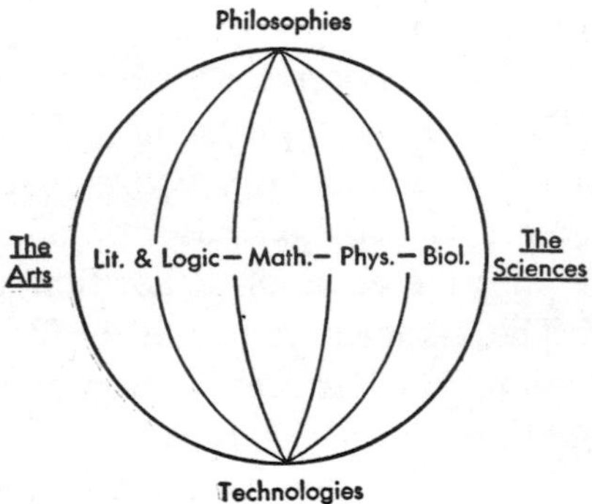

Figure 2. Continuum. The university is diagrammed in terms of disciplines on the surface of a sphere. The disciplines which are used to define the arts and the sciences are arranged in a belt about the equator.

application. For example, chemistry is the theoretical side and chemical engineering the applied side of the discipline that deals with the transformation of matter. Law is the technology which utilizes and applies the analytic and synthetic discipline of jurisprudence; medicine is the technological summation of a constellation of arts and sciences including psychology, biology, and biochemistry; religion is, in part, the technology of theology; advertising and other kinds of propaganda are technological manifestations of art, literature, psychology, and so on.

None of these disciplines is *exclusively* technological or analytic or synthetic. Furthermore, *each discipline is engaged in the pursuit of all three activities*. Thus, if engineering were a discipline which taught only the application of knowledge it would not belong in a university but in a trade school; it would be not a technology but a craft or technique. The same applies to writing, law, medicine, and the other technologies. What gives the technologies equal status with the arts, sciences, and philosophies is that they include the analysis and generalization of their own principles and the utilization of these to control and refine their practice. This is why research is emphasized in all the technologies: research is a term for the application of analysis, synthesis, and reduction to practice in a pioneering way. Of course, it is well known that many of these disciplines frequently do not enjoy equal status in the universities. My affirmation of equal status for them is based on the theoretical argument that they ought to have it, and suggests a conscious departure from current assumptions. Equality will exist only when these disciplines are actually unified into the whole system of the university.

Correspondingly, the arts and sciences, with the theoretical, critical professions, belong in the university because they, too, are engaged in the heuristic enterprise. They place more emphasis on analysis and synthesis than do the technological disciplines, but they also include some reduction to practice: a theory is no good until it has been tested in practice and found adequate. Equally, the philosophies, while emphasizing the synthetic activities, must base their syntheses on analysis and must validate them by reduction to practice. ("Analytic philosophy" is only partial philosophy—indeed, hardly philosophy at all.)

Figure 2 symbolizes the entire field of knowledge and experience classified into the arts and the sciences according to the type of data handled most fruitfully, or the kind of truth communicated, or the kind of conceptual tools best utilized. At the same time the field is classified in another way, according to the emphases placed on *analysis, synthesis,* and *reduction to practice.* Only for purposes of exposition can the categories be sharply delineated.

Philosophy, art and science, and technology are, in that order, decreasingly abstract. But all three belong to a *single system in which all are essential; none is dispensable; and each must be verified by, and thus is dependent on, the other two*. It is snobbish, arrogant, and ignorant to consider engineering and similar "dirty hands" professions as inferior to theoretical art and science. I have seen a critic of art with hands as dirty as any chemical engineer's. He had been restoring some paintings in the course of his studies. He had been in contact with intransigent matter—a vocational pleasure to artist, scientist, and technologist alike.

To ask what meaning is communicated by the poem and by the formula is to ask a difficult question. From the scientific point of view, the meaning of the formula is a property of the statement. It is a property that requires the use of a standard kind of language wherein all the connections between concepts or "constructs" (such as **F**, *m*, and *s*) and perceptions can be made via rules or recipes (which say that if one does A he will observe B and may conclude C)—rules which, because they embody empirical truth and are all interconnected, provide criteria of meaning for the statement. The statement means that connections can be made between formula and related perceptions: it means the truth it conveys. The meaning can be tested empirically, and should be the same to all who understand the language. The meaning of the work of art is the effect it has on us—the response, whether emotional or intellectual, that it evokes in us. A work of art "which has no effects on us means nothing to us, and whatever effects it does evoke constitute its meaning for us."[21] Thus, the meaning of a work of art must be a personal thing, at least in some respects.

Applying these definitions of "meaning" to the formula and poem, I find marked differences between the two. The most striking difference, already alluded to, is that the formula, because of the connotational nakedness(the operational constancy) of the symbols used, means the same thing to all who can read it as a scientific statement, no matter what their language or cultural background. This is not so with the poem—even though the poem chosen for the comparison is rather clear in its meaning.

This point can be made more strongly by considering the opening lines of Part II of T. S. Eliot's "Burnt Norton,"[22] an illustration kindly suggested by Professor Maynard Mack.

Garlic and sapphires in the mud
Clot the bedded axle-tree.
The trilling wire in the blood
Sings below inveterate scars
And reconciles forgotten wars.
The dance along the artery
The circulation of the lymph
Are figured in the drift of stars
Ascend to summer in the tree
We move above the moving tree
In light upon the figured leaf
And hear upon the sodden floor
Below, thc boarhound and the boar
Pursue their pattern as before
But reconciled among the stars.

These lines would perhaps have been more suitable than Francis Thompson's poem for a comparison with Newton's expression, $\mathbf{F}_{\text{gravit.}} \propto (m_1 m_2)\ /s^2$. For just as the formula must be essentially incomprehensible to the reader with no scientific training, so the Eliot poem must be incomprehensible to the scientist with no background or training in literary explication. Yet both have meaning. The meaning of these lines is, in comparison with Thompson's verse, obscure. Indeed, very likely there is no single meaning that would be agreed upon by a congress of literary critics, as the meaning of Newton's law would be agreed upon by a congress of physicists. There is, however, no reason that a single meaning of the lines must be found. The lines are evocative, calling up different responses in different people, and are not intended to convey knowledge.

Thus, we recognize once again the consistent differences we

have found between the arts and the sciences—differences I have tried to bring out through the definitions in this chapter. In defining such terms as "knowledge," "truth," and "meaning," I have not attempted to show all the ways they might be defined, but have tried rather to choose adequate definitions and then have tried to be consistent. It is important to recognize this. Had I chosen other definitions than the ones I used I would very very likely have arrived at similar results, in terms of differences and similarities between the sciences and arts, because the differences and similarities are *there* to be expressed. I am not, of course, sure of this—and if I am wrong, my procedure in defining my terms might be illegitimate—but my alternatives are to be silent when there is so great a need for discussion, or to try to deal exhaustively with each definition, which is manifestly impossible.[23]

CHAPTER 3

On the Scope and Emphasis of Science and Art

Art and science are both universal in scope in that there is no subject that is unfit for the probing insight of the artist, nor is there anything unsuitable for the scientist to examine. The emphases of the two are, however, different. But before we examine why this is so, we need to stress the universal scope of science and art.

There are several reasons why this universality needs to be stressed. First, there is a strong tendency for people to mark out for themselves private bailiwicks into which others may not venture. The humanist is perturbed when the psychologist or anthropologist lays profane hands upon what he considers his special preserve; and the scientist disdains what must, to his special way of thinking, seem ineptitude on the part of some venturesome humanist.

Second, many people suffer the modern disease of partial education, and if they are sufficiently arrogant, they tend to look upon areas of endeavor outside of their own as irrelevant to knowledge and experience. A college functionary who held a minor administrative position and wrote fiction as a hobby once said to me, "I've never had a course in science, and I'm proud of it." One scientist afflicted in this way complained to me about the "humanistic tripe" in the college curriculum, which he wanted removed so that the student, instead of wasting his time studying literature, fine arts, and history, could spend more time on theoretical and experimental physics. An entire school of philosophy, logical positivism, is based on the idea that only certain limited pursuits can yield knowledge. Positivism has been defined as "the doctrine which holds that there is no other logical method than the method of the positive sciences and that what is not accessible to this method is absolutely unknowable."[1] Adherence to this dogma, it would seem to me, is intellectual blindness. Ordway Tead rightly characterizes as the voice of scientific myopia the statement of one physical scientist that "to explain qualitatively today means to explain nothing, means to ignore the developments of some two thousand years."[2] Such a statement portrays the inadequacy and one-sidedness of an approach to knowledge and experience which emphasizes analysis to the exclusion of synthesis. Indeed, positivism, which is now being characterized as "analytic philosophy," is only partial philosophy and, in the sense I use the term, not really a philosophy at all, since it excludes synthesis.

Third, many people who happen to be ignorant about certain subjects feel that they are incapable of understanding those subjects; they fear to acquire even the most basic knowledge in those areas; and frequently they fear and resent those who do have the knowledge. Their fear amounts to willful ignorance. They dare not have an opinion about (for example) modern art lest they be "wrong"; they hold the pronouncements of the scientist to be not only authoritative but incomprehensible to the point of being mystical. In an article on "Scientists and Politicians," published in the *Bulletin of the Atomic Scientists,* Dr. Harry S. Hall comments on the Congressional hearings on the Atomic Energy Act and on the National Science Foundation:[3]

> [Politicians] had a vague, inarticulate understanding that the scientists dealt with abstract symbols. Scientists and others, like General Groves, tried to explain the nature of basic scientific research. Yet, politicians couldn't really understand. Their dim perception of the abstract and sym-

> bolic nature of scientific work was expressed in an indirect way by the use of "theoretical," "visionary," and so forth, to characterize scientists.

They were also confronted, he says, "with the fact that the subject matter with which scientists dealt was, and always would be, a mystery to them." They were permanently barred from gaining knowledge of scientific matters. Consequently, in this respect, they looked upon scientists as members of a sort of secret society from which they were excluded.

> Politicians' perceptions of scientists as a secret society and their resentment of this barrier in their dealings with scientists were clearly voiced by Senator Tydings. After Alvin Weinberg had told Senator Johnson he was wrong in believing that resistance to forward motion in water increased with the depth of the water, Tydings remarked rather bitterly: "Apparently that is one of those scientific facts we are supposed to accept and not ask why." Senator Thye indicated that politicians still held the same view of scientists several years later (1953) in his comment during the hearings on the Bureau of Standards' rejection of the claims made for a battery additive. After Dr. Astin, the Director, had explained the technical grounds for the Bureau's decision, Thye exclaimed: "That is where you have always got us as a scientist, because you can get into that technical field and we are left behind in a daze: we are not sure whether we dare challenge you or not. . . ."

I do not propose that all statesmen should be specialists, able to question scientists on the details of nuclear structure or even of battery additives; but I do feel that they should be able to raise and evaluate questions of principle. A postscript to the battery additive case may illustrate the sort of confusion which might easily be avoided. According to an editorial in *Science*,[4] during one of the hearings Secretary of Commerce, Sinclair Weeks said "that he did not want to 'be accused of over-ruling the findings of any laboratory,' " and added, " 'but as a practical man, I think that the National Bureau of Standards has not been sufficiently objective, because they discount entirely the play of the market place.' " The "play of the market place" is irrelevant to the scientific laboratory findings, which cannot be "over-ruled." Here the natures of natural law and legal law are so confused that a modern King Canute is needed—or, as a less dramatic substitute, adequate education in science—to disentangle them. Knowledge of the nature of scientific objectivity and scientific method might reasonably be expected of non-scientists; they need only dare to seek it.

Finally, the failure to recognize that art and science are both universal in scope has led to a great deal of inferior art—art which imitates science. Although imitation is a tribute to the scientists by the artist, it has been an occupational disease of the artist for the last two hundred years. (Later I shall speak of the constructive effects of science on art.) In an endeavor to bring to their disciplines some of the freshness and vitality they must have found in science—particularly in the early days of the scientific movement—many writers and other artists attempted to imitate science. When a science is young, it is largely analytic in emphasis. Synthesis comes later, after many facts have been gathered and classified. But many artists have not understood this, and not understanding it, what they have imitated is *analytic* science, or partial science. The resulting literature and art, much of it analytic and "objective," is shallow; and while it perhaps accurately mirrors things as they are, it does not provide that elevation of the human spirit which we expect of great art.

From the start, certain superior men saw what was happening and raised warning voices. But the flood of imitative art could not be stemmed and is still running its course: as simple reporting which masquerades under the name of literature; as imitation of young (analytic) social science, describing in detail what people do; as imitation of the young science of psychology, using the technique of stream-of-consciousness. Only the greatest artists have been able to rise above, let alone resist, this flood. And as a result, both art and science have been given bad names.

That art is universal in scope is a concept which the artist needs to implement. He need not compete with the scientist by trying to imitate him, nor give up his claims to the stars or the atoms for fear that the physicist has a monopoly on them. In earlier times, when humanists understood the science of their day, they wrote great books and poetry with its aid. They did not act as though there were a fence around the domain of scientific activity which excluded them.

There is no mystery inherent in science that makes it inaccessible to those with a nonscientific bent. Such people may have to work somewhat harder than others, but the rewards can be proportionately great. Not the least of the rewards is that of being in touch with modern culture. Every serious student of the liberal arts should study as much science as possible, studying some aspect fairly thoroughly. In this way he will be able to desensitize himself to that modern allergy that one specialist has for other specialities, and, more importantly, he will be able to judge accurately the relative value of his discipline, avoiding the mistake that one man's speciality is another man's witchcraft. He will be in a position to make the special insights of the humanist felt in wider realms of knowledge and experience. He will have the knowledge of science without which his use of science must fail. Great art is not independent of science. An artist is implicitly an interpreter of his age, and unless he is in contact with what is going on he cannot produce great art: he cannot "speak to the condition" of his contemporaries with authority; he cannot adequately fulfill all of his functions as an artist—analytic and synthetic. Assuredly, if today's artists do not take the responsibility of understanding modern science and what it accomplishes and of applying their own unique gifts to interpreting it for the rest of us they will destroy art—and themselves. In the part of our culture which should be tended by art, they will leave a vacuum into which will rush tenants of evil repute—anti-intellectuals, propagandists, and special pleaders; ideological morons; self-exhibitionists—and humanity will be the poorer.

The scientist also has problems and responsibilities, though in some respects his job is easier than that of the humanist's. From childhood, he has learned the vocabulary of the arts; and by the time he enters college, his training should enable him to pursue any humanistic interests he may have, though as yet he knows little of the vocabulary, and less of the philosophy, of science. He must still learn the specialized vocabularies of higher mathematics, physics, chemistry, and whatever speciality he is to pursue—a task which requires great effort and helps explain why science is not "easy." It is, in fact, this formidable specialized vocabulary that raises before the humanist who would study science the most discouraging obstacle. These considerations explain why there are many more scientists who are tolerably good musicians, painters, and writers than there are musicians, painters, and poets who are tolerably good scientists. They also pose a challenge to the scientists to correct this imbalance by bringing science to non-scientists.

I have already suggested ways in which the kinds of truth communicated by artist and scientist differ. In pursuing the matter of how the emphases of science and art differ, we must return to the methods of communication and their relation to truth and reality. When scientists and artists operate on the same "subject," often they seem to perceive it so differently that we are tempted to conclude that they are not actually operating on the same thing—that the "reality" is different to each. The scientist may see a tree as a magnificent structure, pleasing to the eye for its color, the form of its leaves and branches, and the architecture by which it has adjusted its need to the stresses of environment. But it may also fill him with wonder and excitement to contemplate the turmoil of photosynthetic activity—each leaf soaking up sunlight, its green pigment utilizing that energy which was in the sun eight minutes earlier to cleave carbon dioxide and return oxygen to the air, and building more trees. The artist may see the tree as a magnificent structure, pleasing to the eye for its form, for the delicate shading of color tones, the play of light on the leaves, branches and trunk, the balanced action of the branches as it leans into the prevailing wind. He may be filled with wonder and excitement as he examines and contemplates, as he tries to apprehend the tree, to capture it in terms of colors, tones, shapes, feeling. Both may use the tree to create a new work, and both, through their "work," must communicate with others.

Consider, as another example, loneliness. A poet might examine the manifestations of loneliness as carefully as a physical scientist might examine the moving pen of a graphical recorder. Both might consider as objective fact the loneliness of a lonely child, but while the scientist would concentrate on describing the chemical composition of the blood, a change in pulse rate, and glandular activities that for him constitute loneliness, the poet or dramatist would concentrate on those aspects whose presentation would convey the feeling of loneliness to his audience.

In some ways it is correct to say that what the scientist communicates is primarily knowledge while what the artist communicates is primarily feelings. Both try to exclude the irrelevant, but neither has any way of knowing whether he has missed something relevant, and neither excludes the other. Yet the aspect of reality which each investigates is in many ways different from that of the other. To understand the differences in emphasis, we must investigate the differences in these aspects of reality.

The nature of reality to poet and scientist has been the subject of a tremendous amount of investigation. As I pointed out at the end of the last chapter, there are many ways of looking at these complicated matters, but for our purposes I shall follow the lead of Professor Henry Margenau and shall use, with his permission, some of the diagrams from his book *The Nature of Physical Reality*.[5]

Suppose that a chemist is investigating a chemical reaction by mixing two colorless substances, dissolved in some solvent, which react to form a colorless third. He may, as the reaction starts, observe the appearance of a color—a color that waxes in intensity to a maximum, than wanes slowly. Along with these color changes he may observe the production of heat by reading a thermometer dipped into the mixture or by feeling the outside of the flask in which the reaction is occurring. He may observe the heat production increasing until the mixture boils, then decreasing until the boiling stops and the mixture cools, with the color gradually fading. All these observations are relevant to the investigation. Irrelevant observations are, for example, that the electric stirrer needs oiling again because it squeaks, that the man at the next bench is humming off key, and so forth.

The scientist generally has no way of knowing whether he missed any relevant data. But other scientists will certainly repeat the experiment if it is an important one, and they may catch relevant matters that he missed. For example, there might have been an accompanying noise that he failed to hear because the stirrer squeaked; or someone else may report observing a different color from the one originally reported—sending both workers to a color-detecting instrument to discover the wave length of the colored light and so determine which report is correct. Although many a discovery begins with an honest mistake of this kind, a large part of scientific training is concerned with learning to avoid the special pitfalls of experimentation. Each of the sciences has its own techniques for minimizing mistakes and certifying the correctness of perceptions.

During the course of the reaction the scientist, besides making observations, makes deductions. Indeed, observation and deduction seem frequently to be a single operation. The scientist deduces that the reaction is going faster from his observation that the mixture has become rapidly hotter and from his knowledge that when a reaction produces heat it speeds up at the same time, thus generating even more heat and more speed. And from other knowledge he has he deduces that the color is an indication of loose combination of the reagents prior to final chemical linkage, since the product is colorless, the color appears only after the colorless reagents are mixed, and the color waxes and wanes along with the increase and decrease of the rate of reaction, evidenced by such things as the production of heat, or the boiling of the mixture.

Now, although no one has actually seen two reagent molecules collide, produce an unstable intermediate which in bulk would exhibit color, and then dissociate into two new products, yet the chemist may believe that this has occurred. It is beyond his means of direct perception. Is it real? Is it true?

The chemist may record symbolically what he thinks has happened in the following way:

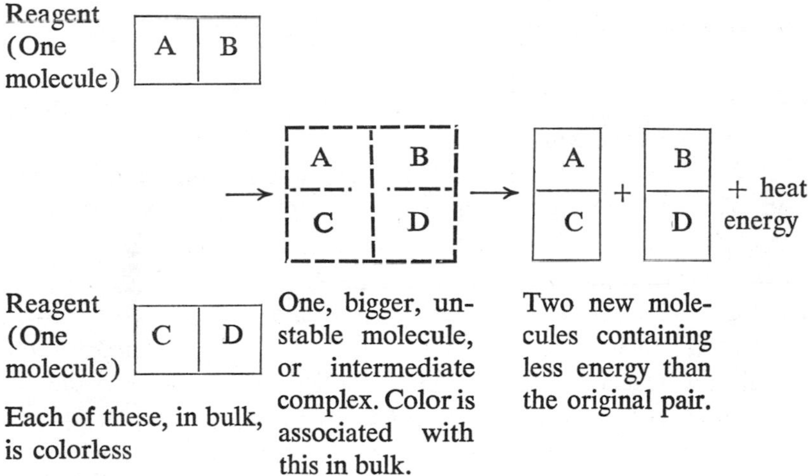

Suppose that he tries to test his belief that this is the course of the reaction. He might separate the two kinds of molecules, AC and BD, from the reaction product and show by chemical analysis that they do have the compositions he has assumed them to have. In a more complicated case, he might have to analyze the products first and then deduce the course of the reactions (a synthetic activity) from the results. He may run the reaction again, but put in twice as much of one reagent relative to the other, and at the end find the excess left over:

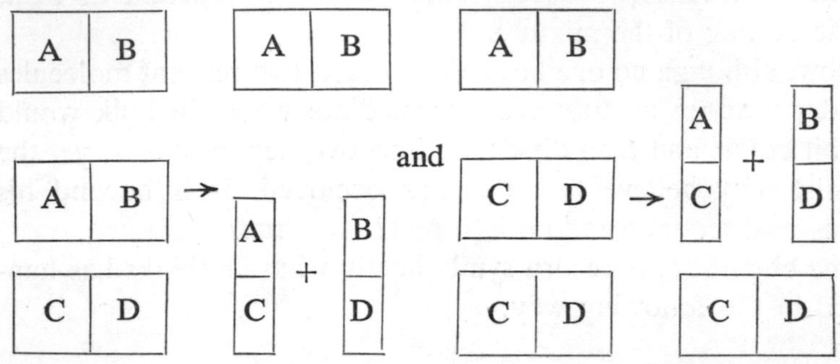

plus heat energy equal to the above per pair of new molecules.

He can then deduce that the unseen intermediate is indeed made up of one of each kind of molecule.

I could proceed to describe the scientist's systematic examination of the experiments, each suggesting other new ones; his constant attempts to make the results quantitative; his attempts to follow the course of an experiment along the time dimension by studying its rate and the factors that affect rate—and so illustrate in detail a good part of his life. But I shall forego such detail and instead symbolize the scientist's activities in order to show what constitutes reality and truth for him.

We can only manipulate *things* in certain ways. We might buy eggs at seventy cents per dozen. We can break and fry such eggs. But we cannot divide seventy pennies by twelve eggs to find out the cost of one. In order to do this, we have first to carry out a "symbolic transformation" in which we abstract from the dozen eggs to the number twelve and from the copper change to seventy and then manipulate these symbols in the desired way. We became adept at such symbolic transformations in grade school, and much of our subsequent formal education in the humanities and sciences consisted of learning more subtle transformations and more complicated rules for manipulation, as well as a great deal of associated new vocabulary. Throughout, we were engaged in the three important activities of analysis, synthesis, and reduction to practice.

The chemical experiment illustrates these activities. The experimenter has more or less shallow perceptions: he sees the substances, feels the increase in temperature, senses the changes with the passage of time. Simultaneously, on the basis of his training, he makes the symbolic transformations which enable him to write symbols for molecules and to manipulate these in such a way that a reasonable course for the reaction is written down. So far, analysis and synthesis have gone hand-in-hand. He now tests his hypothesis of the intermediate complex by reducing it to practice in the further experiments which were described.

This kind of sequence has been generalized by Professor Margenau in the following way. All the observations which we make, being close to and limited by our means of perception, are in that sense shallow. Since they are gained through our senses, we can symbolize them as lying on a plane, the "plane of perception." In Figure 3 this is shown in cross section as the line *P*, which may be thought of as a section through a plane extending from behind the page through it and out towards the reader, cutting the page along the line *P*. Our perceptions are imagined to lie on or close to this plane, and to the left side of it in the figure.

The symbolic transformation which I described above is shown by a pair of lines, a pathway, so to speak, to the circles, which represent constructs. The pairs of lines are recipes, or "operational definitions," by which one can proceed from the perception to the construct. (I use the term "construct" instead of "concept" because what it represents is in a sense "constructed" by a kind of abstraction or translation or transformation process or by an act of invention.)

The double lines say, in effect, that if one will follow the recipe, or do the experiment, he will make observations which

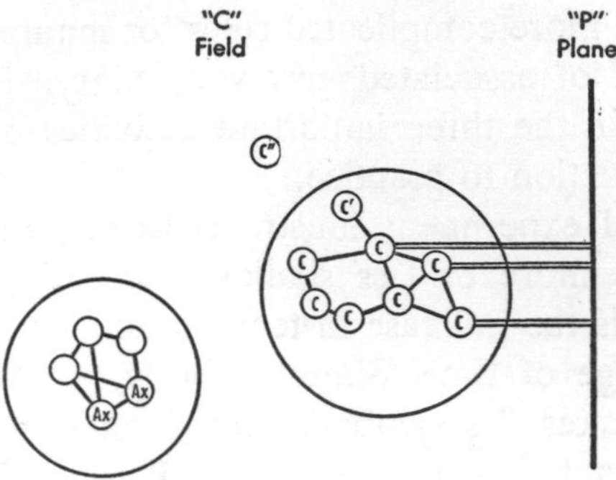

Figure 3. Diagrammatic representation of the "plane of perception," constructs of various kinds (C), connected and insular (C″), and theories (groups of connected constructs enclosed in a circle). The figure is redrawn, with permission, from Henry Margenau, *The Nature of Physical Reality: A Philosophy of Modern Physics,* figures 5.1 and 6.1.

will lead to the designated construct. In the chemist's experiment "molecule," "energy," and "wave length" would be constructs. Anyone who has tried to follow a recipe knows that a good deal is involved in the process. One must have the ingredients and the tools and must know the language in which the recipe is written. One may still fail if the recipe is incorrectly given or if one's technique is not adequate to the task. A good deal of a teacher's time is spent showing the student how to make this kind of symbolic transformation, and a good deal of a research investigator's time is spent learning or inventing ways to devise a better recipe or to get hold of a better construct.

Some of the constructs are not connected directly to the *P* plane but are connected to others which lead eventually to the *P* plane. These connections are shown by single lines to differentiate them from the recipes. They, too, are rules, but logical rules arrived at by logical processes. Sometimes, they are stated in words, but they are best stated mathematically. In our chemical example the intermediate complex would be one of these constructs. A single line—which specifies that one molecule of AB reacts with one of CD—connects that construct to other constructs (molecules of AB and CD) which in turn are connected by double lines to the *P* plane because rules of chemical analysis tell us how to recognize and measure these substances. The intermediate complex would be connected by single lines also to AC and BD, and these would be connected to *P* by double lines because they, too, can be determined chemically by analysis. Our hypothetical intermediate complex, then, is connected to the P plane via the reagents which produce it and the products it yields.

In a sense, then, the construct "intermediate complex" is further removed from the plane of perception than the reagents or products. So are all the constructs, logically connected, which are derived from, or constructed out of, each other. As long as any construct has two or more connections to others, it is a relevant part of the scheme, since it leads somewhere. On the other hand, a construct like *C′* in Figure 3 is scientifically useless because logically it leads nowhere. *C′* might symbolize an aesthetic pleasure we experience through the blue color produced in the experiment, but this does not affect the scientific validity of the experiment.

The scientist will accept as empirically true the theory (in the large circle) about these multiply connected constructs: the *truth* receiving its strength from the nexus of logical interrelationships indicated by the single lines. That the truth is *empirical* truth is confirmed along the operation pathways to the plane of perception. The construct *C″* is unconnected and therefore irrelevant, as is *C′*, which is singly connected.

Scientific reality is symbolized by the empirically true theory and associated parts of the *P* plane.

Figure 3 shows a theory isolated from the plane of perception and made up of interconnected constructs, two of which are identified by *Ax*'s. These *Ax*'s represent axioms—logical inventions—upon which the theory has been constructed. Provided that the rules of logic have not been violated, such a theory is logically possible and *formally true*.

Somewhat over a hundred years ago three mathematicians—C. F. Gauss, N. I. Lobachevski, and J. Bolyai—began, independently, to investigate the kinds of geometries which might be constructed by, in effect, denying some Euclidean axiom.[6] As we all know, Euclidean geometry adequately fits the world we live in. Surveyors, architects, lawyers, scientists, and engineers all confirm its applicability or truth. This mathematics is based on axioms or postulates which, although unproven, were derived from the everyday experiences of surveyors, astronomers, and construction engineers—men whose knowledge must have been great, since it enabled them to build the great cities of ancient times. Some of these axioms state that a large sphere is geometrically similar to a small one (this defines the kind of space we live in), that the interior angles of any angle add up to 180°, and that through a point outside a given straight line there can be drawn only one straight line parallel to the first. These axioms, as we know, fit our experience: a large equilateral triangle is similar to a small one; all pairs of parallel lines are similar in that the corresponding angles (alternate angles) made by a straight line cutting both parallel lines are always equal (Figure 4).

Euclidean space has been called "flat" space to distinguish it from other kinds of space in which not all the Euclidean postulates hold, but which are nevertheless thinkable—thinkable in geometrical, quantitative terms, though not necessarily capable of being pictured to our senses. One such space, named Reimannian, after the mathematician who first conceived of it, is called spherical space. In such space, straight lines return upon themselves. There are no parallels. The sum of the interior angles of a triangle is always greater than Euclid's 180°, and the sum is a larger number for large triangles than for small triangles, so that all triangles, large or small, are dissimilar in the Euclidean sense. Another type of non-Euclidean geometry, Lobachevskian, deals with "pseudospherical" space, and herein the interior angles of triangles add up to less than Euclid's 180° (see Figure 4).

Such imaginative system-making is a delightful enterprise for the mathematician. What is more, some of the systems invented without reference to the factual world eventually turned out to

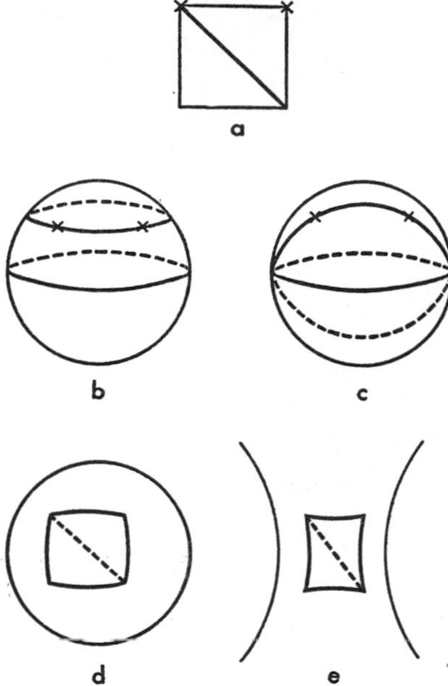

Figure 4. The shortest distance between two points on a surface is a geodesic line. In Euclidean geometry this is our familiar "straight line" —as between the points *x* and *x* in *a.* In *b,* the line connecting *x* and *x* along the latitude line is not a geodesic line. The shortest distance on the surface is along the arc of a great circle, as in *c*. Thus, shortest distances do not yield parallel lines on the surface of the sphere. In *a,* the interior angles of a triangle add up to 180°. The sum would be greater than 180° on the surface of the sphere, as in *d,* and less than 180° on the surface of the pseudosphere, part of which is shown in *e*. These diagrams are merely for rough illustration. To follow this fascinating subject further, see H. G. and L. R. Lieber, *Non-Euclidean Geometry*; *The World of Mathematics,* especially the essays by W. K. Clifford, "Mathematics of Space and Motion" and "The Postulates of the Science of Space," and H. von Helmholtz, "On the Origin and Significance of Geometrical Axioms"; and George Gamow, *Matter, Earth and Sky* (Prentice-Hall, 1958), chapter 21.

have unexpected applications in the world. For example,[7] Riemannian geometry was useful to Einstein in connection with the theory of relativity because it seemed applicable to astronomical space, wherein distances are very great. Such an application, however, does not make Euclid obsolete because for terrestrial spaces, in which distances are small compared to astronomical distances, the consequences of Riemannian geometry become indistinguishable from those of Euclidian. We cannot concern ourselves here with the details of non-Euclidean geometries. Many of them are easy to understand, and some are intriguing exercises in wit and logic.[8] Their connection to my theme lies in the fact that they started as *formally true* systems. Some of them become empirically true as well after physicists found connections between them and the plane of perception. The effects of these discoveries on the art world will be suggested later.

The more accurate the predictions of new phenomena or constructs that follow from a theory, the more reliance can be placed on its scientific truth.

As a simple example,[9] let us imagine that we hear the sound of a bell in the distance. We wonder how the sound energy gets from the bell to us. We go and feel the bell and realize that when it is sounding it is also vibrating. Suppose we have already verified the construct "air," and we set up the hypothesis (a small and tentative theory) that the vibrations of the bell cause, by suitable energetic coupling, pulsations in the air, and these carry the sound to our ears. Then we are able to predict that in the absence of air we shall not hear the bell ring. To test our hypothesis, we hang a bell in a jar and start it ringing while we pump out the air (Figure 5). As the air is gradually removed, the sound of the bell dies out even though we can see the clapper hammering. Then we let the air back in. As we do the sound grows louder.

We have now traced the circuit of an ideal kind of proof of truth and reality. We started at the plane of perception, hearing the bell ring, seeing and feeling it. We developed constructs such as pulses of air and the velocity with which these pulses travel. We deduced that were we to remove the air we would observe a new connection to the *P* plane in that the sound would fade. We carried out the experiment and verified the set of propositions which connected our constructs. (This sequence is simplified for purposes of exposition. Actually, the sound of the bell fades while there is still some air in the bell jar because the bell and the air have become energetically uncoupled. This does not invalidate the point of our argument, however.)

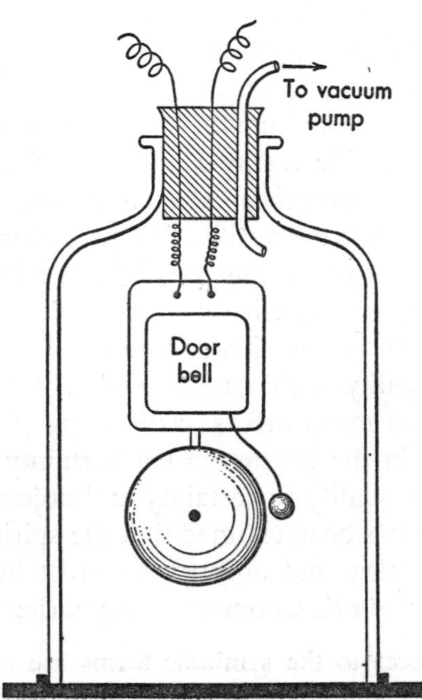

Figure 5. Setup for an experiment with sound. An electrical bell is placed in a jar or bottle so that it hangs by the thin wires, which do not transmit much of the sound. The jar, open at the bottom so that the bell can be put inside, is sealed at the bottom with a plate. Air can be pumped out or readmitted through the tube at the top.

The act of verification requires the circuit from perception to construct, to other constructs, by logical processes (symbolized by the single lines in Figure 3), and thence back to the *P* plane. We need not pursue the more subtle question of how accurately the prediction must be borne out, what with experimental and inherent errors in the necessary operations. The main point is that a prediction can be made and fulfilled. This circuit gives some verification to the constructs in it: they become verified facts. But the verification has more weight the greater the number of connections to other constructs and to other regions of the *P* plane than can be made—whence a tendency of scientists to lose interest in established facts and to be much more interested in making new connections between constructs. An important part of verification requires that other scientists be able to repeat the operations with the same results.

Reality to the artist or humanist often means something different from the scientific reality I have described, though there are certainly some connections between the two kinds of reality. We might suppose that the verification procedures—particularly the requirements that something predictable arise from a theory and that the reality be objective in the sense that other qualified people can also verify the theory—would not be a necessary characteristic of reality in the artistic realm. Yet this supposition is not acceptable to many artists, critics, and philosophers, who feel that there is in the greatest art a certainty and objectivity that is of the same quality as certainty and objectivity in science.

For example, it has been claimed that the spiritual significance of religious art is clear not only to the artist but to his patron and audience. Ananda K. Coomaraswamy writes:

> The references to the symbolic forms are as precise as those of mathematics. The adequacy of the symbols being intrinsic, and not a matter of convention, the symbols correctly employed transmit from generation to generation a knowledge of cosmic analogies: as above, so below . . . The archetypal house, for example, repeats the architecture of the universe; a ground below, a space between, a vault above, in which there is an opening [the luffer] corresponding to the solar gateway by which one "escapes altogether" out of time and space into an unconfined and timeless empyrean.[10]

This suggests that there may well be a precision about the artist's symbolic transformation which is *functionally* as great as that achieved by the scientist, though the artist's symbols differ in appearance from the scientist's and cannot be manipulated in the same way as his—that is, by algebra and geometry, and so forth. And certainly there are theories of reality associated with this symbolism and the truth it conveys that are not identifiable with physical reality.

One such theory, of great weight and antiquity, is illustrated schematically in Figure 6. According to this philosophical theory, there is an imperceptible, "primary" reality. This primary reality,

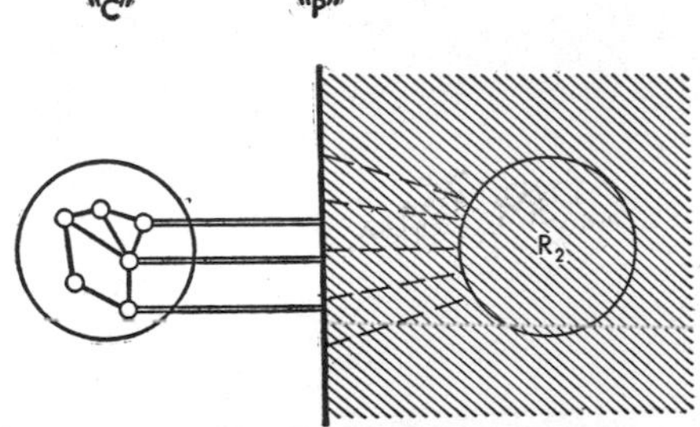

Figure 6. Schematic representation of a theory (a nexus of constructs—see Figure 3) in the field of physical reality, shown to the left of the plane of perception (*P*), and of a hypothetical reality, R_2, to the right, which in some way is connected with the emergence of data on *P*. The figure is redrawn, with permission, from H. Margenau, *The Nature of Physical Reality*.

R_2, brings about the emergence of data on *P* (compare with Figure 3). This presumed reality is reminiscent of the "essences" of Platonism and represents a theory which retains some weight today, though not in scientific circles. Whatever the status of R_2, it cannot be identified with physical reality because it is incapable of meeting the scientific verification procedures. However, the existence of such a reality, not accessible to direct perception yet not intrinsically unknowable, may be a proper subject for consideration within the mansions of the humanities, whose disciplines have always been hospitable to subjective and introspective experience, and whose tools and techniques may be able to discover and tell us about such "reality."

In ancient times it might reasonably have been argued that the sound of our bell was the voice of Euterpe. Can this Muse of music and lyric poetry be considered a "construct?" Clearly, there are connections with other such "constructs," for she was one of the nine muses who presided over the arts and sciences: Calliope, Muse of poetic inspiration, eloquence, and epic poetry; Clio, of history; Erato, of erotic poetry; Melpomene, of tragedy; Polyhymnia, of the stately hymn; Terpsichore, of choral dancing;

Figure 7. *The Muses,* woodcut, by Pencz (1535). The Muses are "pitying the fate of Germany." Figure 308, p. 274, in *Iconographie de L'Art Profane* by Raimond van Marle (Martinus Nijhoff, The Hague, 1932).

Thalia, of comedy; and Urania, of astronomy. And there were further connections. The nine were daughters of Zeus and Mnemosyne, the goddess of memory. These muses had meaning for thousands of persons at one time (Figure 7), and their powers have been transmitted to us through our language, as the roster of their names shows. (And it is attested by the names of eight of the muses, attached to eight streets in New Orleans.) Perhaps "they" still exert an influence from the field of R_2 in Figure 6. Certainly, the artist is free to bend this kind of reality to his own uses. But lacking the operational rules and correlations to the *P* plane, they cannot be certified as real in a *scientific* sense.

I have contrasted scientific truth, as truth-about, with artistic truth, as truth-to. The latter "refers to the kind of thing that people (presupposing a certain degree of esthetic sensitivity and in many cases some training or background in the arts) can verify in their subsequent experiences of the arts and of the world, in the form of enriched and renewed perception (or perception for the first

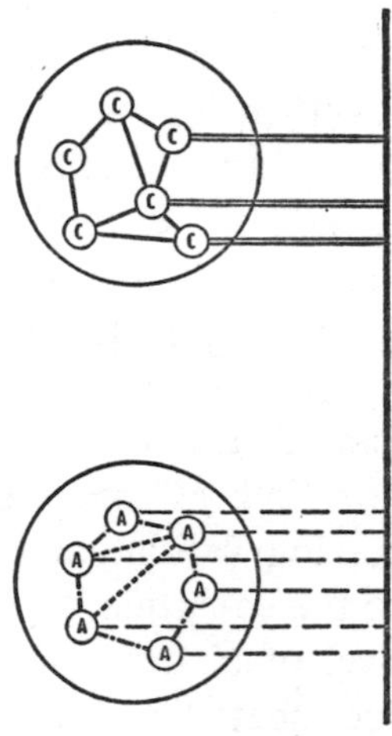

Figure 8. Schematic representation of reality in the realm of knowledge and experience. The diagram is meant to suggest that in the field of the arts there is a reality comprising the plane of perception which corresponds in many ways to physical reality (see Figure 3). There are the *analogs* of constructs ("C" in the physical, "A" in the arts field) which are connected in their own ways and *analogously* yield theory. There are thus *functional* similarities in the presence of differences in appearance.

time)."[11] It contributes to *acquaintance with,* as distinct from *knowledge* of, reality. The reality conveyed here is true-to felt experience; it involves the "conveyance of the looks, taste, feel of things: the enrichment of our affective life and the sensitizing of its perception."[12]

Figure 8 shows a schematization of these kinds of reality, suggesting the themes that will recur throughout this book: that the sciences and humanities are both universal in scope but different in emphasis and that there are functional similarities despite differences in appearances.

As previously shown, data on the *P* plane become "knowledge-of" in the hands of the scientist: facts verified through multiple interconnections. Concomitantly, such data can produce in us "acquaintance-with" phenomena—from common, simple, immediate awareness to the more subtle forms of awareness which the artist is able to evoke in us. In some way, perhaps, the artist's work may correspond to the higher levels of abstraction that characterize the scientists' theories and constructs. The artist may have a technique for conveying as reality to another person love, hate, or loneliness. He may, for example, present such feelings on the stage by means of a drama which is convincing only if it creates *real*, natural processes in the audience—whereupon it is regarded as good art. The presentation may fail due to some "experimental" defect such as a poor actor or an outside disturbance. The "message" or "moral" may be comparable to the scientist's "theory," receiving validation as it is conveyed to the critics or audience. Like the scientific "theory," the artistic "message" is on a higher level of abstraction than the constructs or the drama, which are connected to the perceptions.[13] Much of the reality conveyed by the poet or other artist seems to be of this kind. Both this reality and that of the scientist include data from the same sensory *P* plane.

Like the scientist, the artist "constructs" his works. Out of his experience and knowledge, he selects what is relevant to his creation of poetry, music, literature, painting, arabesque, dance, and so on. He seems to see not as other men see. "The artist picks out of reality something which we, owing to a certain hardening of our perceptions, have been unable to see ourselves."[14] Let us compare some opinions about this act of construction, with its elements of abstraction, symbolization, and invention, as it is carried out by scientist and artist.

The physicist utilizes a construct "space" (which could be one of the *C*'s in Figure 3)—a special kind of space. To the layman, who abstracts from his own experience, there is not exclusively one kind of space, but there are a visual space, a tactile space, and other private kinds of space. But constructed space, the space mathematically defined in equations of physics, says Margenau, "towers above these others by virtue of a postulated unformity which . . . both welcomes and in a large measure defies the onslaught of immediate experience."[15]

Listen to what the philosopher F. H. Bradley has to say in a discussion of criteria of historical criticism. He points out that the historian cannot accept passively what his evidence and testimonies give him. He has to exert himself and to labor to interpret, for in itself the evidence is only "a host of jarring witnesses, a chaos of disjointed and discrepant narrations."[16] This surely implies the same sorting, judging, and inventing activities by which scientists create constructs, as presupposed in the quotation from Margenau. The quoted phrase, "a host of jarring witnesses," must certainly ring true to many an experimentalist as a description of some of his data!

Indeed, this sort of history is close to descriptive science: it is a kind of liberal art which shares the same criteria of truth as science but includes emotion in its purview. Here we see that construct formation is not unique to science.

What, then, of the connections among constructs and the connections to nature which are shown in Figure 3? Recapitulating, the scientist endeavors to connect constructs, one with another, and with nature. The connections among constructs are logical ones: they tend toward quantitative statement, they function as agents for prediction, and one of the important enterprises of the scientist is to multiply and also to simplify them. Further, a construct achieves validation through connections, via other constructs, to nature; and hence, a construct with only a single connection to nature or to another construct is useless from a practical standpoint and from that of theory, since it leads nowhere. But a system of interconnected constructs constitutes a theory. Do we find counterparts of these connections in the humanities?

I suggest that the individual work of art may be taken as the analog of the construct. Is it connected to others? Does it lead anywhere? Are there multiple connections? Does it furnish an aid to prediction? Is theory possible? I turn to the art critic Henri Focillon for an answer. In speaking of styles and the phases through which they pass he says:

> The successive states through which they pass are more or less lengthy, more or less intense, according to the style itself: the experimental age, the classic age, the age of refinement, the baroque age. These distinctions are perhaps not wholly new, but it must be borne in mind that —as Waldemar Déonna has pointed out in a penetrating analysis of certain epochs in the history of art—these ages or states present the same formal characteristics at every epoch and in every environment. This is so unmistakably the case that we need not be surprised in noting close similarities between Greek archaism and Gothic archaism, between Greek art of the fifth century B.C. and the sculptures of the first half of the thirteenth century A.D.; between the flamboyant, or baroque state of Gothic, and eighteenth-century rococo art. This history of forms cannot be indicated by a single ascending line. One style comes to an end; another comes to life. It is only natural that mankind should revaluate these styles over and over again, and it is in the application to this task that I apprehend the constancy and the identity of the human spirit.[17]

The tracing of connections lends validity and importance to the individual piece, and if the connections are made along the strand of time, so are all such connections. They exhibit themselves as a pattern later, when the whole tapestry is viewed. The connections that can be made among several cultures further reinforce the fabric of theory.

The language in which these connections are stated may be strange to the scientist, but he cannot fail to recognize that if the connections are not quantitative, they are none the less real. In place of equations connecting constructs, we have qualitative statements describing relationships. These deal in a coin which, for its qualitative impression, has wide circulation and a high purchasing value. Tracing similarities and analogies and changes in style in various art works and assigning them positions in some historical chain of styles—say, experimental-classic-baroque—establish the connections. Not being an artist, I shall do no more than try to sketch the meanings of these logical connections.

Turning once more to the historian we see a similar pattern emerge. The knowledge gained by the historian is inferential or reasoned, and he also has rules of method and canons of relevance by which to judge his data. Arnold Toynbee has pointed out in the Introduction to *A Study of History* that the method of history consists in viewing and presenting some of the facts of human life, by recourse to certain fictions and by the elucidation of general laws.[18] His fictions, such as "the Press" or "public opinion," or personifications, like "England," ought possibly to be taken as constructs. He has gathered, evaluated, and classified an enormous amount of historical information which he has organized on the basis of hypotheses. From the resulting magnificent sweep of events, relationships, and ideas, he has extracted general laws the operation of which illuminate and at the same time govern the *History*. The gathering of data, its evaluation, the construction and testing of hypotheses constitute a method of science, and if patterns appear in the data their constant recurrence must be meaningful.

The historian-philosopher R. G. Collingwood takes the position that these patterns are not necessarily given by the data, certainly not in the same sense that data in the physical sciences yield directly to logical manipulations.[19] On the basis of much the same data, he points out, Kant, Hegel, Comte, Marx, and Spengler derived different patterns which they extrapolated backwards into the poorly known past, and forward into the unknown future in unjustified and blind analogy to the methods permissible in natural science. Though what Collingwood says is true, it is also true that no scientific theory or pattern is necessarily given by the data. In fact, on the basis of much the same data, Newton, Copernicus, and Ptolemy derived different patterns for the solar system. However, there were available techniques for validation which, when they could be applied, yielded clear answers and supported Newton.

If I understand their views correctly, these historians' conception of historical reality bears resemblance to Margenau's conception of physical reality in that constructions or interpretations of data (subject to review at any time) are connected by relations which in a sense test and validate each other and the whole, being also connected to available data. On this methodological point historians might all agree, and physicists, too. Speaking of historical reality, Margenau says:

> Past sense impressions of the sort here treated [e.g., Whether Joan of Arc really heard voices] became occurrences which constitute a conjectured temporal course of an objective universe. Thus they are constructs and need to be verified as such . . . The process of empirical verification still has its circuital form, with one occurrence suggesting another and finally driving the inquiry into the realm of the immediate, which in the present case may well be an ancient text or a phrase in a document.[20]

There is a difference between the *A*'s and *C*'s of Figure 8: whereas the *C*'s receive verification through multiple interconnections and eventual connection to the *P* plane, the *A*'s need be connected to the *P* plane only. One reason for the difference is that the scientific theory conveys empirical truth by means of propositions, and propositions must be connected logically to ensure that there are no contradictions present. A single contradiction that stands up against all tests can destroy a theory; so all constructs and connections must be consonant with each other and adequately connected to the sensory *P* plane.

But the *A*'s do not primarily convey knowledge. Therefore, they do not contradict each other.[21] They simply *are*. The works of Beethoven do not invalidate those of Bach. In fact, each may enhance our appreciation of the other. In my opinion, the artist is judged by the success with which he achieves the purpose of his work, and not necessarily by some validating logical connection to other work of his or of someone else.

I venture to conclude, then, that the data of the sciences and the arts differ as the kinds of conceptual tools used by scientists and by humanists differ. The major differences in data are, indeed, like those separating any two specialities, but the situation is complicated by the specialized terminology each uses. For if it is clear to a scientist that his friends in the arts do not understand the subtleties of his special language, modest wisdom would counsel him to assume that he may not understand the subtleties of their statements, which otherwise sound like English to him. Although the meaning of the Thompson poem may, at first reading, seem clear to anyone, a critic who knows the life and times of Francis Thompson might have much of importance to say in explication of it. We see, in addition, that while the constructs of the physical scientist are different in their quantitative precision and connotational barrenness from the qualitatively rich creations of the artist, yet there are correspondences in function. And there are certainly similarities in their requirements for clear relationships to nature. As far as data are concerned, both art and science are inherently universal in scope.

The physical scientist has been singularly successful in gaining control over part of the perceptual world through his manipulation of naked symbols and constructs which defy "the onslaught of immediate experience." The humanist also endeavors to grasp with his conceptual hands such constructs as mass, energy, form, things in motion, attitudes toward them, and so on. He does not exclude spontaneity, feelings, desires, and such. Rather, he tries to use them, together with other parts of his experience, to produce a whole work of esthetic stature which may be greater than his experience in that it creates participation (to use John Dewey's phrase) of others in his isolated and singular experience.[22]

Both artist and scientist, in their own ways, pit themselves against those barriers that isolate persons.

CHAPTER 4

Methods of Science and Art

I have suggested that scientists and humanists come close to each other in some of the methods they use. In this chapter I shall examine how closely they approach each other by looking at their methods of discovery, of invention, of experiment, and of isolation of variables. We shall also examine some of the differences in their methods.

Discovery and Invention. It is often difficult to distinguish invention from discovery. Although in discovery, one comes upon, so to speak, what has already existed, the process may have creative aspects. Invention is by its nature the creation of something new. The difference between the two, some think, is solely a matter of the person to whom it occurs. To the inventor, things come together "inside" him; if they came together in his subconscious, the result might appear to his conscious self as a discovery. Discovery involves the recognition that things come together "outside" the discoverer. Discoveries are often made by following up a deduction or by pursuing an analogy. Inventions often seem to burst suddenly out of analogies or to appear by a process called induction. In any case, acts of invention and discovery may occur in many and complicated ways.

Artist and scientist are at no time more alike than when they are engaged in their creative acts. For then both are stripped of the regalia which mark their professions, both are groping human beings engaged in an act which appears to verge on the divine.

The poet Paul Valéry, speaking of the man whose profession is writing, says that part of the process of invention is that moment of illumination wherein the mind senses something new.[1] The illumination carries with it the conviction that with sufficient effort the full import of the revelation can be worked out. The philosopher-mathematician Henri Poincaré describes several instances in which the solutions of problems came to him suddenly and unexpectedly—once as he was in the middle of a conversation and about to put his foot on the step of a bus. The solution appeared certain to him, and he continued his conversation. In another instance "the idea came to me, with just the same characteristics of brevity, suddenness and immediate certainty."[2] The composer Mozart found that under certain circumstances, "when I feel well and in a good humor, or when I am taking a drive or walking after a good meal, or in the night when I cannot sleep," his mind would be crowded with melodies. He would sort them out, and, inventing a theme, he would find melodies linking to the theme and to each other, until eventually a finished composition would exist in his mind. The beauty of the composition and the fittingness of the related parts would be clearly evident. Later, he would have to work each part out in detail.[3]

If I may add a first-hand experience to this list, I can report that suddenness combined with an immediate sense of the fitness of my idea. While I was listening to a piano concerto, the idea suddenly occurred to me that it should be possible to prepare electron exchange polymers. I was at once certain that this was feasible, and I felt the fitness of the idea in complementing the already well-known proton exchange polymers. These latter were not known by that name, and the conventional methods for examining them experimentally were different from those that would have to be used with the electron exchangers. But once the symmetry of the relationship became apparent to me I experienced great pleasure and excitement.[4]

Many writers, both artists and scientists, agree that one of the powerful rewards—and perhaps a powerful driving force and guide in these creative acts—is the satisfaction of a sense of beauty, the satisfaction of a certain aesthetic sensibility. Of course, there may be other drives—the desire for recognition or for promotion, the feeling of urgency produced by epidemics, ideological dangers, war—which contribute to discovery and invention. But these do not minimize the sense of pleasure and of the fitness of things that an invention or discovery can produce. Democritus said, "I would rather find a single causal law than be King of Persia," and J. J. Becher wrote, "the chymists are a strange class of mortals impelled by an almost insane impulse to seek their pleasures among smoke and vapour, soot and flame, poisons and poverty, yet among all these evils I seem to live so sweetly that may I die if I would change places with the Persian King."[5]

A great deal has been written on the nature of invention, and nowadays there is much study of the creative process with a view to learning how to recognize potentially creative people and how to set up conditions which increase creativity. As far as I can see, there is no marked distinction between the way creative thoughts come to scientists and the way they come to artists. At this level of endeavor an intrinsic, human potentiality is functioning.

Experiment. Although experiment has been strongly associated with the sciences in much modern writing, actually both the sciences and the humanities use this important method of gaining knowledge and experience. The subjects and the objectives of experimentation may be different in the two cases, but the method is the same. Here is Henri Focillon on the subject:

> Indeed it is nowhere possible to behold more clearly than in Gothic architecture how, from a given form, there are derived to the very last detail the happy issues that affect the structure, the organization of masses, the relation of voids to solids, the treatment of light, and even the decoration itself. No graph, apparent or real, could be more

> plainly indicated. It would be a mistake, however, not to recognize in this graph the action of an *experiment* at each of its crucial points. By experiment I mean an investigation that is supported by prior knowledge, based upon a hypothesis, conducted with intelligent reason, and carried out in the realm of technique. In this sense it may well be said that Gothic architecture is guesswork and reasoning, empirical research and inner logic all at once. The proof of its experimental character is in the fact that, in spite of the rigorousness of its method, some of its experiments remain almost wholly without results; in other words, much was wasted, much was barren. How little do we know of the innumerable mistakes that lurk in the shadow of success![6]

Earlier in the same essay, Focillon speaks of

> the preliminary sketches of painters who, seeking the accuracy or the exact beauty of a movement, will superimpose the drawing of several arms upon the same shoulder. Rembrandt's sketches swarm across Rembrandt's paintings. The rough draft gives vitality to the masterpiece. A score of experiments, be they recent or forthcoming, are invariably interwoven behind the well-defined evidence of the image.[7]

We need hardly discuss experiment in the sciences, for there is no succinct definition of method that surpasses that just given by the critic of art: *"By experiment I mean an investigation that is supported by prior knowledge, based upon a hypothesis, conducted with intelligent reason, and carried out in the realm of technique."*

Many examples of experiment can be drawn from the field of literature. Here, preliminary sketches also "swarm across" the autograph manuscripts. Figure 9 shows part of a page from Keats's "Hyperion," called to my attention by Professor Frederic G. Cassidy. There evidently remain in this revealing document the traces of the experimentation through which the poet sought the perfect expression of his vision. There is a feeling for the right word and phrase: "an eagle's wing" is changed to a "young

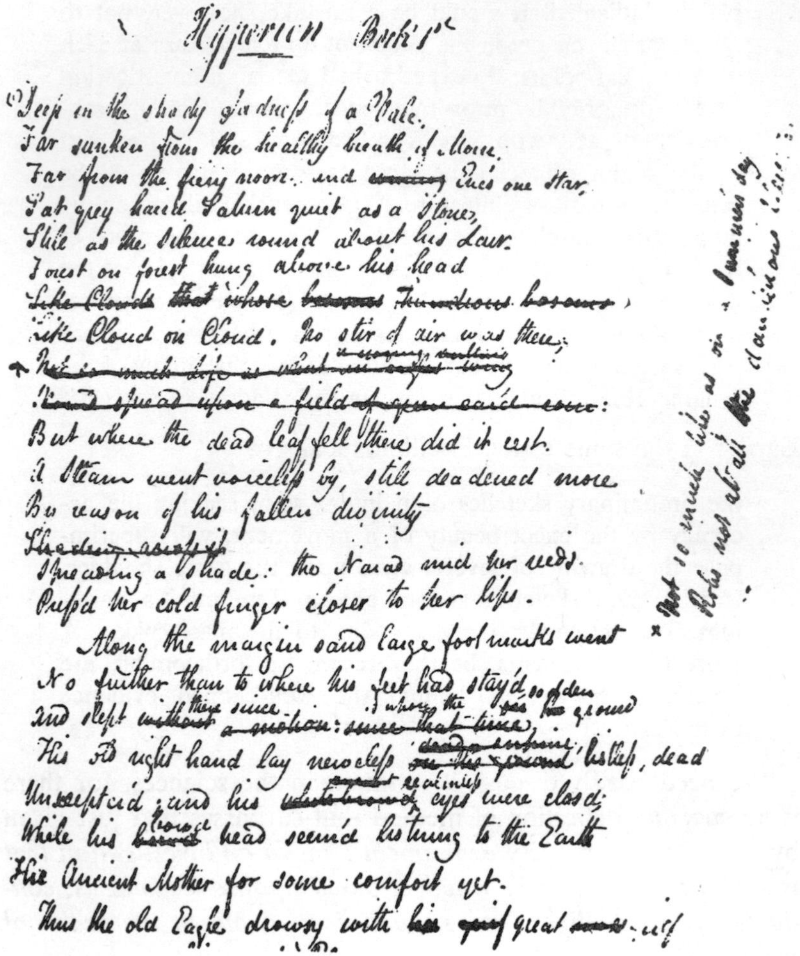

Figure 9. Copy of a sheet from the autograph manuscript of Keat's' "Hyperion."

vulture's wing." But for some reason, which may have had to do with scansion and possibly also with the connotations of "vulture," the two lines:

> Not so much life as what a young vulture's wing
> Would spread upon a field of green ear'd corn

are erased and replaced by the marginally written lines:

> Not so much life as on a summer's day
> Robs not at all the dandelion's fleece.

But these are still not entirely satisfactory, and we find the last of the two lines changed in proof:

> No stir of air was there,
> Not so much life as on a summer's day
> Robs not one light seed from the feather'd grass,
> But where the dead leaf fell, there did it rest.[8]

The objectives of experimentation are, of course, different for art and science. The artist experiments to achieve that perfection of form and style that gives qualitative precision to his product. But in the process he may, as I shall show later, generalize; for, frequently, one of his aims is to bring out something universal or traditional through his work. The scientist experiments to remove the unique, to eliminate the particular and uncontrolled variable—in other words, to achieve maximum generality. Both use a technique described by one of the greatest of experimenters, Michael Faraday, in these words: "Let the imagination go, guarding it by judgment and principle, but holding it in and directing it by experiment."[9]

Isolation of Variables.—The experimental approach to a problem often begins with an attempt to isolate the variable factors which may control the phenomenon under investigation. This is done by varying one factor, or a limited number of them, at a time to find out what aspect of the phenomenon each factor or variable controls. This is the basis of the analytic approach to a problem; and a general rule of procedure in the sciences is to try to alter but one variable at a time, observing the results when the experiment is repeated with no other changes in it. But as one tries to carry out this rule more and more efficiently, thus presumably measuring the effects of a change in variable more and more accurately, the interconnectedness of things becomes increasingly evident; and the scientist, enmeshed in the web of connectedness, finds that he must deal with many changing variables at once. This difficulty has forced the development by scientists of special techniques of many-variable analysis, which is an area where analysis and synthesis fuse. Nevertheless, for most purposes—certainly in the physical sciences—the isolation of variables is a practical possibility and a powerful tool.

Among the humanities, the difficulty of isolating variables is obvious. A work of art cannot be considered a mere summation of isolable properties. The properties cannot be isolated; the whole of a work of art is always greater than the mere sum of its parts. To isolate a property of a thing is to some extent to destroy its nature, and the destruction becomes more marked as the property is wrenched from a whole whose properties are more intimately connected.

This is perhaps one of the chief sources of misunderstanding between humanists and scientists. "How," asks the artist who does not understand science, "can these scientists talk of isolating variables, when the world is one, and to isolate a part is to destroy in some measure the whole? Do not philosophers such as Whitehead and Hocking emphasize the togetherness, the interdependence of things?"[10]

The point is made rather nicely by Reed Whittemore, in a short poem entitled "Purity":[11]

Ah, purity,
And the purists,
Talking,
Talking of hearts that are pure
And an art that is pure
And an earth that is not at the moment but should be
Some day
Pure.

Talking, talking,
Talking in what would appear to be total ignorance
Of the following simple, pure fact about purity: purity
Is as rare in its purest state
As the absolute vacuum

Of which the physicist speaks in his classroom when somebody
Knowing too much suggests that all falling bodies
Do not fall equally fast.
"But they would," the physicist says, "they would if you took
All the air away."
All the air away?
Who would take all the air away? Is there anyone,
Anyone present, anyone living,
Who would make such an issue of purity that he'd take
All the air away?
I must meet him.
I must shake his pure white hand and say to him, "Blast!
If you take all the air away you'll fall equally fast."

A myopic scientist, on the other hand, not understanding the difficulties and importance of qualities, could be led into acts that would be ludicrous were they not so dangerous—acts, for example, like prescribing for the individual person on the basis of statistical calculations.

The sources of misunderstanding are removed if we once more advert to the functions of description and analysis and of seeking connections and synthesis. Isolating variables in analytic science or analytic humanities is no problem. Critics make a living at this. An example, taken from the field of stylometric analysis, will show how valuable the isolation of variables can be to the humanist. The music critic Ernest Newman, in an essay on Beethoven, speaks of the successes of stylometric analysis:

> The dominant style-elements of many writers from Cicero onwards have been brought to light by style-analysis. Emile Hennequin demonstrated long ago Flaubert's unconscious tendency to follow a certain pattern of construction, from word to phrase, from phrase to sentence, from sentence to paragraph, from paragraph to chapter, from chapter to book; while in a brilliant essay he laid bare the verbal elements that constitute the style, and therefore give us clues to the thinking, of Victor Hugo. More recently, Alphonse Le Du has shown in minute detail Hugo's unconscious proneness to certain rhythmical pat-

terns in both his poetry and his prose. W. F. Jackson Knight has subjected Virgil's accentual symmetries to a similar analysis; and more than one writer has demonstrated the curious ways in which a verbal image in Shakespeare will not only beget a cognate image but call up from the depths of his subconscious, by some strange unforeseen compulsion of its own, a side-line of thought which had certainly not been part of the poet's conscious purpose when he began.

Undoubtedly there exists in the composer also definite irresistible biases towards certain basic formulae personal to him . . .

Of all the composers whose work I have studied from the stylometric point of view, I have found Beethoven the easiest to systematize, the one in whom the unconscious inclination towards typical melodic-rhythmical formulae is most marked—a fact which of itself, considering the towering greatness of the man, should dispose of the innocent notion in some quarters that to demonstrate these biases in a composer is to lower him in some way in our estimation. There is probably some subtle organic reason for the formation and fixation of these unconscious biases in the artist; possibly they represent a sub-surface effort at economy on the part of the artistic faculty, the establishment of broad, smooth, charted highways, as it were, in his thinking that enable him the better to concentrate on the intellectual adventures he will seek and find on the road.[12]

In the isolation of variables we can see important features of method. The initial phase of such an enterprise, whether in the sciences or the humanities, is descriptive or analytic. From descriptions of observed similarities and repeated patterns comes the idea that there must be reasons for them. The scientist might think in terms of a mathematical correlation; the humanist might assume that there is "some subtle organic reason." At this stage, the work has already become integrative, synthetic. But it cannot properly cease until, by the circuital processes schematized in Figure 3, the scientist tests his equation, the critic his "subtle organic reason," by making a prediction. The scientist must predict what a change in variable might do, and the critic must predict which melodic sequence should follow this introductory phrase if the derived pattern of "irresistible biases" is correct. When enough evidence has been piled up to give the theory adequate validity, the work has passed into the stage that may be characterized as philosophical. Here indeed, the artist referred to above would have a right to ask how one can talk of isolating variables when to isolate a part is to destroy in some measure the whole. His concern would measure the skill with which the artist had combined his brush strokes, with which the scientist had reconciled his variables and adjustment-parameters, and with which they had utilized or corrected "the innumerable mistakes that lurk in the shadow of success."

Some Remarks on Methods. When we speak of the methods used by the scientist or the humanist we must specify whether we mean the methods used by a given worker as he does his work, or the methods that appear to an analyst who compares many workers' methods and generalizes from the comparison.

Scientific and humanistic methods vary with the training and temperament of their practitioners. The analyst of method may say that the scientist proceeds by gathering data to test some idea or hypothesis, which, ordinarily, he has developed by analogy. He tests the hypothesis against the data, devising experiments to obtain the data. He makes predictions from the hypothesis and tests these. If the predictions are not borne out or if the data do not fit the hypothesis, he must first examine the experiment to see if mistakes have been introduced; or, if the experimental results stand up, he must suitably alter the hypothesis and test it further. The scientist is alert for new phenomena which may appear in the course of the experimentation and for any new leads or analogies to follow up experimentally or theoretically—the net results being valid additions to the body of knowledge.

This analysis of method, being constructed after the event has occurred, represents the logical rather than the psychological aspect of experiment, as the chemist James B. Conant put it.[13] The psychological aspect was well described by Professor Joel Hildebrand in his Edgar Fahs Smith Memorial Lecture in which he compared the scientist with a problem to a man trying to enter a room.[14] He may open the door and walk in. If the door is locked, he may know of a key which, made by someone else, but procurable, will let him in. If this is not possible he may be able to pick the lock, or he may learn of some feature of the type of lock which will enable him to pick it. If this is not successful, he may consider pulling the pins out of the hinges and lifting the door off bodily. But perhaps none of these work; yet he wants to get into the room. He may attempt to break the door down. Some problems are stubborn. Let us suppose that the door to the room is sturdy, and does not yield to considerable battering. Our man may make at least three choices: he may keep on battering at the door; he may become discouraged and give up trying to enter the room; or he may become interested in some other, nearby door. Judgment is required to decide when to stop beating against a locked door. Some workers will happily match their own stubbornness against the intransigence of inanimate matter, while others will heed the advice of that great humanist W. C. Fields: "If at first you don't succeed, try, try again. And then quit. There is no use being a dam' fool about it."

The writer, the composer, the musician, the architect—all follow similar methods in attempting to solve their problems, as we have seen in Figure 9 regarding the poet, and in the quotation from Focillon regarding the architect. Their methods all bear a resemblance, a resemblance which is not fortuitous.

The history of science has shown that the problems which are insoluble to one generation may become soluble to the next. Thus, one cannot call any problem inherently insoluble without a risk of being shown up as a fool. Nevertheless, it is a wise man who can judge when he has done his best, and, returning to our man who wishes to enter the room, we can see that he would be wise to drop the project if the door will not budge after his best battering. He can always turn to another problem, possibly a related one, which may teach him new ways of picking locks and thus encourage him to return to the original recalcitrant problem, or may reveal a new passage to the room which was inaccessible to frontal assault. Once in, he may easily be able to learn how to open the original door. Or, he may never get into the original room.

While this account illustrates the way in which a scientist may attack a problem, all creative workers attack problems in about the same way, though their methods differ in details. The difference in the methods of workers in any given discipline is as great as that between workers in different disciplines.[15] It is seldom, if ever, that an individual worker creates by a formalized application of heuristic techniques, though he may solve routine problems in this way.

The History of Differences. Beating of drums and shouting of slogans generally herald something new. When methods and insights are new, frequently their inventors or discoverers and their practitioners emphasize their differences from the old. One of the reasons for this emphasis is the difficulty of interpreting the new through the language of the old. This is a legitimate reason for some kinds of jargon.[16] As people learn to understand the new, they begin to see its similarities to the old, and the emphasis on differences subsides. It is not simply that people become so familiar with the new that it loses its novelty. Rather, their understanding of it allows them to see how it is genuinely new and how it is not. This understanding presupposes a knowledge of the past, as well as a present security.

In the arts a "reaction" is that emphasis on differences which begins this sequence of events. New styles "react against" old forms, often representing an extreme departure from the old. But sooner or later they grow less extreme, revealing similarities to the old.

E. F. Haskell has pointed out that this sequence of events occurs only in cultures which change rapidly.[17] In cultures which change slowly, new things depend for their very life on seeming not to be new at all. Science is a motive force in increasing the rate of cultural change, but even in science changes which are both new and far-reaching may require for their acceptance emphasis on similarity with what exists rather than emphasis on their all too obvious differences.

When they were young, the physical and biological sciences formalized an approach to the gaining of knowledge which, though it seemed totally new, was not entirely so. The formal procedure of science—in Bacon's metaphor, putting Nature to the question, torturing her by experiment to wring forth answers to the questions—seemed to be unique. But actually, elements of the method had been in practice here and there for ages. Bacon, and later Descartes, formalized and developed scientific method, raising the concept to a high level of abstraction and generalizing it, so that after them what was truly new in the method was plain for everyone to see *and to apply to all sciences.*

Nothing is static. The new interacts with the old, and both are influenced. As understanding of the new develops, de-emphasizing differences and narrowing the gap between the new and its precursor, the new and the old influence each other. It is not the vacuum that Nature abhors but the grand discrepancy of which the vacuum is, so to speak, one manifestation. As we understand the evolving methods of science better we become more aware of their ancestry in other disciplines. And we see also that the methods of other disciplines adopt those parts of scientific method that are useful to them.

Some Actual Differences. There are, in fact, authentic differences between the sciences and the humanities regarding the methods they employ, the nature of their constructs, and the areas of knowledge and experience in which they operate. Compare, for example, the historian and the natural scientist. The quarry of the historian is the store of events which have happened or are happening. Although a certain course of reasoning may lead him to predict the existence of a certain bit of information, or of a document, which he may be led to find (and have to validate), he cannot have recourse to the same method of experiement as the natural scientist. Moreover, the historian, unlike the scientist and to some extent like the humanist, is *particularly concerned with concrete, individual occurrences which took place at a certain location.* The scientist is usually more interested in abstractions and universals (his constructs are generally of this kind) which in some aspects are independent of special times or locations.

A good deal has been made of this difference. It is perhaps an underlying theme in the philosopher Ortega's discussion of historical reason, which he considers more rational, rigorous, and exigent than "physical reason" because it accepts nothing "as a mere fact," but endeavors to see "how it comes about."[18] Putting Ortega's statements into our language, his point seems to be that since the physical scientist deals with constructs and emphasizes the relations between these abstractions (which Ortega calls "facts," e.g., "impact," "attraction") rather than their causes, in the sense of R_2 in Figure 6, he does not come into contact with reality in the intimate way that the historian does when he sees how his "facts" come about in the individual instances of history. But at any rate the ideal of one discipline need not be that of another.

One facet of the matter is illustrated by Poincaré in his essay on "Science and Hypothesis":

> Carlyle has somewhere said something like this: "Nothing but facts are of importance. John Lackland passed by here. Here is something that is admirable. Here is a reality for which I would give all the theories in the world." Carlyle was a fellow countryman of Bacon; but Bacon would not have said that. That is the language of the historian. The physicist would say rather: "John Lackland passed by here; that makes no difference to me, for he will never pass this way again."[19]

Assessing this criticism we would say Carlyle is talking descriptive history; Poincaré criticizes him because as a mathematical physicist he habitually thinks in law-formulating terms. To lessen the possibility of conflict with historians and to increase mutual understanding we could rephrase Poincaré's sentence to read, "That is the language of the historian exercising his descriptive function. The [synthetic] physicist would say . . ."

The sciences and the humanities have been compared with respect to what has been called the expendability of their constructs. Great art, music, literature, and poetry of the past gave answers to problems which are still with us—renewing themselves with each generation. There are always new answers to these problems, answers which, when they are true, seem to enrich but rarely to displace the old.

In the sciences, a new construct may cause the revision of an entire theory or, more rarely, of an entire science. But what was true in the old science remains true in the new. The constructs created by Galileo eventually brought about the revision of astronomical theory and much of the science of that day. The complex of constructs which make up Einstein's theory led to a revision fully as great, all the results of which are not yet apparent. But what was true in Galileo's theories and in Newton's remains true today, though comprehended at a higher level of abstraction in the larger synthesis which is Einstein's theory.

To new facts there is usually some resistance which at its best has a conservative influence by putting the burden of proof on the new. At its worst, it becomes an idolization of some aspect of the past. What happens in these processes is, of course, symptomatic of the particular times. It is only the true parts of great art and great science that remain true throughout time (though the errors are certainly *preserved*). But because they are true it does not mean that they are understood. An art, literature, or philosophy which is fragmented, divisive, and withdrawn from truth (perhaps into some personal dream world) bespeaks a sick artist.

The scientist sometimes appears to draw his data from a more restricted field than the humanist or artist. The restriction is, broadly speaking, a result of his method, which insists on generalization combined with quantification and testability. Within this restricted field, however, the scientist penetrates to a depth which is limited only by the instruments he uses or his own native senses. The practitioner of the arts uses methods that bear close resemblance to those of the scientist. But when he deals with the peculiarities that make up individuals or single occurrences, or when he moves into the realm of the subjective, and especially when he approaches the ineffable and endeavors to weave about it the bonds of symbol, then he is far from the preserves of science.

CHAPTER 5

Results: I

Objective-Subjective; Quantitative-Qualitative; Discursive-Presentational; Theoretical-Esthetic.

When we consider the similarities and differences between the humanities and the sciences in terms of the kinds of results that they produce from their data by their methods, the most fascinating notions and hints appear. Some are dim—the mere "shadow of a shade." Others are more clearly seen. Still others show the definite outlines of marketable products. Indeed, they are so numerous and elusive that I am tempted, in Ortega's phrase, "prudently to lay down [my] pen and let a flock of questions take off on their winged course."[1] But being committed to imprudence, I shall examine some of these notions, trying to impart some flavor of their interest and to show how widely they occur.

Let us begin by reconsidering Figure 1. On the one side we have the sciences, on the other, the arts, connected by a continuum so constituted that some property accentuated in one area fades off toward the other, is inverted along the way, and appears as the opposite kind of property accentuated in the other area. The figure is not intended to convey any quantitative notions. It simply contains an hypothesis, by no means new, which we shall use to organize this chapter and the following one. That it can successfully organize a good deal of data suggests that it contains elements of truth.

In this and the following chapters we shall examine some of

the contrasts which are commonly said to characterize the sciences as compared with the arts. There will naturally be some overlapping of data and of results covered, and the arbitrary nature of the selection will become apparent. Throughout the two chapters, I shall speak in broad terms, occasionally using "artists" in place of "humanists," particularly when speaking of certain modern movements.

OBJECTIVE-SUBJECTIVE. One difference between the sciences and the arts lies in the extent to which an observer's own motives, interests, desires, and idiosyncrasies become involved in the process of dealing with his data. The scientist tries to be objective. It is so well-known that one almost apologizes for reiterating it:

> The kernel of the scientific outlook is a thing so simple, so obvious, so seemingly trivial, that the mention of it may almost excite derision. The kernel of the scientific outlook is the refusal to regard our own desires, tastes, and interests as affording a key to the understanding of the world. Stated thus badly, this may seem no more than a trite truism. But to remember it consistently in matters arousing our passionate partisanship is by no means easy, especially where the available evidence is uncertain and inconclusive.[2]

This must not be taken to mean that the scientist is a sort of neutral or passive entity. Far from it. We should not confuse with true objectivity that air many scientists assume of lofty neutrality which is frequently merely apathy—a result of intellectual sloth and one of the greatest sins that can be committed in the name of scholarship of any kind, humanistic or scientific.

Objectivity has two sides: a private and a public. The first may be described as the impartial approach to the fact, a disinterested approach, the approach of a true judge. The approach is impartial, yet the scholar has a point of view. Practically anyone who carries out an observation must have some point of view—some implicit or explicit hypothesis, based on knowledge, which he is putting to the test. He almost always has a notion of what he is looking for, though he tries to remain sensitive to the unexpected, the chance occurrences.[3] This means that he always has a philosophy of some kind, however unfocused it may be, and it means that absolute *personal* objectivity is a myth. Scientific objectivity requires this kind of impartiality, which in true scientists represents the operation of high ethical principles.

The progress of science does not rest solely upon the judicial disinterestedness of the individual scientist. What is called "scientific objectivity" is a part of the grand method of science. No matter how scrupulous, well-meaning, and careful an individual may be, he may still err without knowing it. He may be led astray through the "delicate duplicity" of things. Therefore, he must always be open to criticism. This is the public aspect of scientific objectivity. Scientific objectivity is the result of free criticism and of cooperation by many scientists.[4] Along with this critical attitude, which accepts no "authorities" in science, there is the cooperative effort to speak the same language, to make communication effective. These bases of scientific objectivity—personal disinterestedness, free criticism among scientists, and striving toward mutual understanding—are not inevitable developments of society, but are hard-won positions which are ours only as long as we cherish them. They are continually being challenged, and we must continually maintain them.

Since scientific objectivity is not dependent solely on the activities of the individual scientist, a scientist may hold as passionately and tenaciously to his theories as he wishes. But he must not be, for any period of time, in a position to set up a new dogma by the suppression of criticism of his ideas by others, or by the enlistment of political or military force.

The great prestige that science has achieved has tended to draw to it some adherents of doubtful repute. As long as true scientific objectivity can be maintained as a condition for the correct use of the term "science," there is little to fear from these groups. But one must look askance at anyone who claims the validity of experimental fact for any other kind of knowledge, however arrived at. Such a claim involves confusion of levels of abstraction; it involves confusion of the *P* plane with the constructs of Figure 3. As an example of this unforgivable sin, Edward Haskell cites Stalin's affirmation, in *Dialectical and Historical Materialism,* that "our theory has the validity of objective fact."[5] The sin is unforgivable because it is incorrigible as long as it persists. The confusion of levels makes it incorrigible, for objective fact is the court of last resort for a theory; here the court's authority has been conferred on the defendant; and the theory thus becomes immune to the correction which is nature's forgiveness.

The emphasis I place upon scientific objectivity is not intended to disparage other ways of certifying knowledge and experience that belong to fields other than the scientific. Emphasis on the objective "infallibility" of science—usually an emphasis of a pseudoscientific kind—has brought in some quarters a reaction against science. This is reflected in the writings of Unamuno[6] and Ortega,[7] for example. Unamuno speaks much of the need for passion, individual expression. "Science robs men of wisdom and usually converts them into phantom beings loaded up with facts."[8] If he had only said "purely analytic science" he would be correct. Another passage in the same essay, ". . . neither ought love of wisdom to lead us to a renunciation of science, for that would be equivalent to mental suicide, but to an acceptance of science as a preparation, and as nothing more than a preparation for wisdom" would also be correct if "science" were qualified with "analytic." Note for the record that in this sense the (analytic) humanities, too, are a preparation, and nothing more than a preparation, for wisdom. There are great areas of experience which the scientist does not claim to be able to survey scientifically. Wisdom is greater than knowledge and experience and requires as a precondition both scientific knowledge and the knowledge and experience sought in the humanities.

In general, then, scientists strive by all the artifices possible to attain an objective approach to knowledge and to bring more and more domains of data under this rigorous and ascetic regime.

The humanities, however, need not exclude the subjective ways of gaining knowledge. Under the onslaughts of science, they have unfortuately given ground, relinquishing territory which they might with more wisdom (which includes true knowledge of the nature of science) have defended and occupied. As a scientist, I would welcome a more vigorous showing on the part of the humanistic disciplines, provided it did not reside largely in efforts to retreat to the past. Such a change could strengthen our universities and our whole culture if it were to come about in wisdom. After all, the scientists are not the only ones who have such a firm hold on the future that they do not fear to let go of the past.[9]

Objective and subjective may also be given another reference, and may be contrasted. They may refer to works, empirically verifiable in the former instance, and cognitively or emotionally based, but not able to be empirically verified, in the latter. The sciences and the arts have been contrasted in these terms. However, when we compare theoretical scientists with their counterparts in the liberal arts, the contrast virtually disappears. Thus, a mathematician might develop a theory (such as that based up axiom *Ax* in Figure 3) which is incapable of being tested. Subjective criteria *alone,* that is, mathematical judgment and proofs, can determine its (formal) validity. Like Riemannian geometry, such theories may, by being connected to perceptions, become scientific reality; but until that happens they are only subjectively validated. This has been the history of many theories. Einstein's theory of relativity, and certain predictions based on it, were held in such esteem before being tested that the most troublesome and costly efforts were made to put them to a test. For example, on the basis of deductions from his theory, Einstein, in 1916, predicted that if in 1919 telescopes were set up in Africa in the path of an eclipse and photographs of a certain star were taken, the position of the star would be found shifted by 1.75 seconds of arc (a tiny, but accurately measureable shift). Relativistic calculations had indicated that the light from the star when passing close to the sun would be bent from its normal straight path because of the tremendous gravitational field of the sun, but that this could only be seen during an eclipse. The experiment exactly confirmed the prediction. The predictions made on the basis of relativity theory about atomic energy have been overwhelmingly convincing, and have allowed power plants to be built which behave as the relativity theory says they should. Indeed, such accurate predictions have come to be considered almost commonplace by laymen, and it is only after one considers the fabulous amounts of money, effort, and time that are expended on political and economic predictions, the reliability of which cannot nearly compare with the scientific ones, that the latter can truly be brought into perspective.

So we see that there are formal, theoretical constructions which the scientists may hold in high esteem without their having been certified as empirically true by connections to the *P* plane of Figure 3. To such formal work in the sciences *corresponds* in a logical way (though the two are differently based) purely subjective art in the arts. Here, moods and emotions are "represented" or called forth by compositions which apparently correspond to nothing objective. The products of the arts may also be tested for structural correspondence with phenomena, which is the criterion of objective truth in the sciences. Lewis Carroll, a formal scientist, wrote literature which in many ways approaches pure subjectivism. His nonsense verse reaches it. He worked competently in both the sciences and the arts, and specialized in abstractness in both.

QUANTITATIVE PRECISION-QUALITATIVE PRECISION. To some extent, the sciences and the arts differ in the emphasis that they place upon quantity and upon quality. But that difference is not absolute, and once more we can find similarities between the methods of these two great areas of knowledge and experience. In the search for qualitative and quantitative precision different symbol systems are used. Certain constructs of physics and chemistry—constructs like electron, mass point, atomic orbital—can be expressed *precisely* in words only with great difficulty, if at all. The same is true of certain philosophical, artistic, and religious concepts—inspiration, the soul, grace—which cannot be expressed *literally,* but only metaphorically. The physical constructs can be stated with precision by mathematical symbols and used in logical manipulations. The precision results from the connotational barrenness of mathematical symbols. The philosophical, artistic, and religious concepts can also be represented symbolically—and as precisely as possible—in poetry, pictures, music, and other media. But there does not seem to be any relation between the two symbolisms.

When I say that a mathematical symbol is connotationally barren, I mean that it is barren of the connections with sensory experience and figures of speech which words may recall. The symbol does, however, have precise *implications*—it implies what it represents and how it may be utilized. The sciences have always sought precision of measurement and statement. These are essential to the scientific method and closely related to scientific objectivity. Nowadays, however, the claims to precision of the physical sciences are not absolute, as they once were. In an earlier day, the physicist Lord Kelvin could write:

> When you can measure what you are speaking about and express it in numbers, you know something about it, and when you cannot measure it, when you cannot express it in numbers, your knowledge is of a meager and unsatisfactory kind. It may be the beginning of knowledge, but you have scarcely in your thought advanced to the stage of a science.[10]

This statement still holds, but we no longer expect absolute exactitude from measurement. The expectation has changed. The development is an interesting one and typical of what happens in the sciences.

It was once assumed that all that was necessary to obtain greater precision of measurement was to exercise more care in measuring, to use increasingly more refined instruments, and to make larger numbers of observations. However, it was found that as one actually does take more and more measurements of a given phenomenon, as the data pile up, the value of the *mean* of the results can be determined with increasing precision, converging on some value which represents the mean of an extraordinarily large number of measurements and may be designated as the "true value." But one does not have to take such a large number of measurements to find the true value; one can calculate it from a smaller number, since, as data accumulate, the precision with which the true value can be calculated increases systematically. The set of measurements is said to show internal convergence when such systematic behavior is observed.

Suppose now that a more precise value is desired. The same phenomenon may then be measured with a more sensitive device—instead of with a ruler, say, with a traveling microscope, which magnifies the object and compares it with a magnified scale. Again, a mean value of the measurements would be obtained, with increasing precision as more measurements are made. The values obtained by the less crude measurements should fall closer together and should be within the range of values of the cruder measurements, in which case one says that there is external convergence of the different measurements (see Figure 10). The discovery of this kind of convergence led to the assumption that all one had to do to obtain greater precision of measurement was to use finer measuring devices. However, it has turned out that when the measuring device is made so sensitive that it probes down to molecules, atoms, and subatomic phenomena, a limit of precision appears—often with a relatively large, irreducible error—and external convergence to a "true value" of the quantity being measured cannot be guaranteed. This happens whenever the measuring instrument, whatever it may be—an X-ray or electron beam, for example—destroys or changes the system in the process of measurement.[11] These phenomena, described crudely as showing the haziness of nature, are of the greatest importance in the realm of the very small—of molecules and nuclei—though for ordinary objects their effects are inconsequential. Similar difficulties arise in

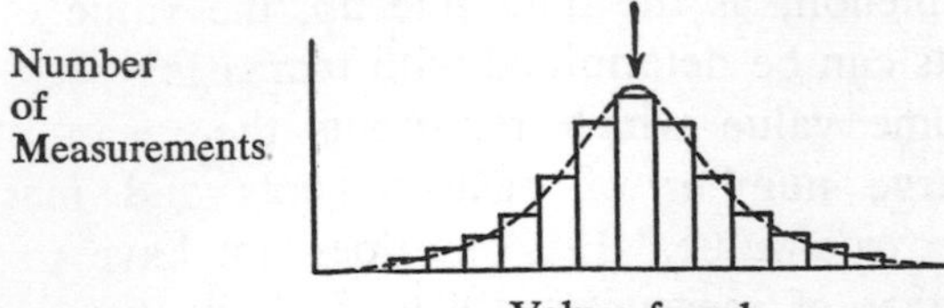

Scatter diagram of measurements of relatively low degree of precision.

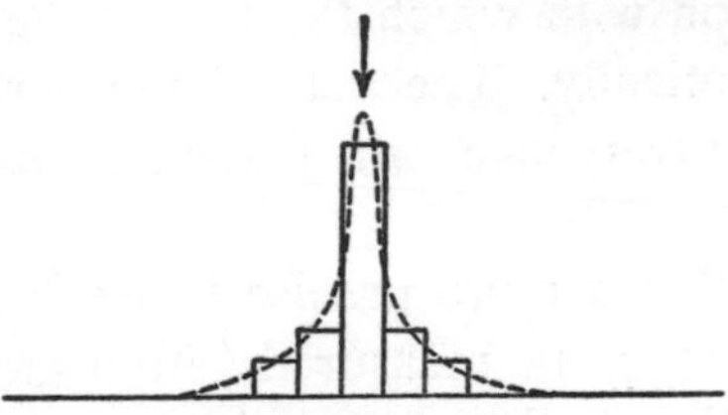

Scatter diagram of measurements of relatively high degree of precision.

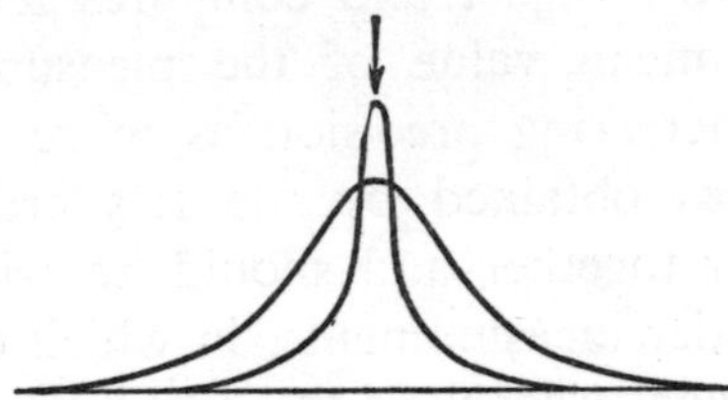

Superimposition of the curves when there is external convergence.

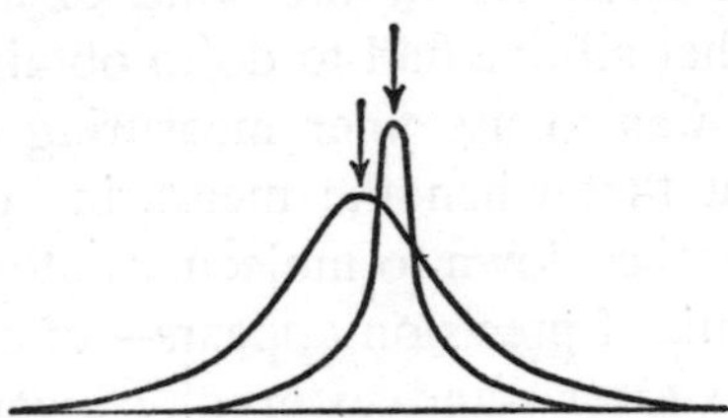

Superimposition of the curves when there is not external convergence.

Figure 10. Phenomena found in endeavoring to obtain increased precision of measurement of a given object. Arrows indicate means. The blocks or rectangles in the upper two diagrams indicate by their height the number of measurements that fall within the spread of values that the widths of the blocks cover. The diagrams show that fewer and fewer measured values are found farther and farther from the mean. The smooth curves of the lower two figures indicate the regularity of this relation.

connection with the study of living organisms which are killed in the process of examining them. The greatest precautions have to be taken by psychologists, sociologists, and anthropologists against the effects of the tools used on the persons or societies under study, lest the conclusions be hiddenly biased.

Our concern is less with the actual measurements than with the effects of these factors on thought. Thinkers as different as Ortega, Russell, and Margenau have taken note of them. Modern science began with the Copernican revolution, which dethroned man and his world from the center of the cosmos by establishing that the earth revolves about a sun which itself is only one of many stars in the firmament. Thereafter, the study of nature through experiment and measurement further tended to objectify and dehumanize the world. Scientists did not look for the purposes in things. Subjectivity had no place in the scientific description of the world. During the late eighteenth century, however, Immanuel Kant, by setting up a contrast between inner experience and the outer world, effected what Bertrand Russell calls a "Ptolemaic counter-revolution" which restored man to the center from which Copernicus had dethroned him.[12] A further development, an outcome of the surprising results of pushing the quest for precision far enough, led to the discovery of indeterminacy, or "vagueness," in nature. Man had thought that what was to be known was in a sense absolute and that his knowledge, though relative to this absolute, could come arbitrarily close to it by progresssive refinement. But now the absolute has been taken away, and physical theory has been changed by the relativism of Einstein. Now "reality" is relative, and *our knowledge* is absolute, as Ortega puts it.[13] In Margenau's symbolism, the constructs and their connections are *exact* and, in this sense, absolute; uncertainty resides at the plane of perception. But the Copernican revolution continues; for the possibility that there may be a large number of habitable orbs in the universe, where sentient and intelligent beings may reside, again raises the question of the central location of man. These ideas about relative and absolute will have to be clarified to be meaningful, but I shall do so in a later chapter.

It is often argued that a discipline is a science only to the extent that quantitative precision can be attached to its data. If this is true then the scientific component of behavioral and social sciences is presently small. The difficulty in attaining precision in these disciplines is one of their most formidable troubles. One has only to read the searching analyses that are made in setting up experiments and in describing results (as collected, for example, in *Psychological Theory,* edited by Melvin H. Marx[14]) to realize how great these difficulties are. Social scientists are committed, as aspiring scientists, to the derivation of laws with ever-increasing generality and precision; yet, by the very nature of their material, that intransigent datum, the human being, is continually obtruding himself. To take his individuality into account is to recede from generality; yet to crush him with the Juggernaut of theory is to be untrue to *social* science. (It is an easy way out only for the myopic theorist.) Difficult though it is, the problem is not necessarily insoluble. Perhaps, a new kind of symbolism will be needed. In any case, that a situation is complex is no reason for thinking that it cannot be described in terms of laws.

As we consider the arts the picture changes. The kind of precision that the artist seeks may be designated as qualitative. The artist attempts to state a particular perception—be it an observation, feeling, or insight—in such a way as to communicate its quality as precisely as possible. Of course, his aim may be merely to present the perception and relieve some stress within himself. The results may be of the kind described by the philosopher William Ellis, who says of the Greeks that "their poems were an emotional play of words around ideas as yet too unfamiliar to be caught in explicit statement."[15] Or he may try to make a subtle and many-sided examination of the perception. When precision of this kind has been carried to an extreme by writers and other artists, (analytic) precision indeed results, but there can also be great emptiness.[16]

Side by side with qualitative precision in the arts there can be quantitative precision. In music, the pitch and duration of notes are specified with a high degree of quantitative precision—volume with less precision. In dance, speed, distance, and direction are quantitatively precise. There is a limited amount of quantitative precision in poetry and a great deal in architecture.

Correspondingly, a qualitative precision of the highest kind is required in many sciences—in chemistry, zoology, anthropology, and so on. Actually, the two terms qualitative and quantitative are not mutually exclusive except when defined in an extreme way. They serve us well in this section, however, by allowing us to demonstrate in still another way that the arts and sciences, while the scope of each is universal, differ in emphasis. For example, psychologists and anthropologists do not exclude *any* words whatsoever from their data and allow in their theories words with the richest connotations. But, unlike the artist, they try to limit these words to cognition and try to avoid their arousing emotion in the investigators. Thus, inclusiveness of data is similar for some scientists and humanists, but the similarity ceases with respect to involvement of the practitioner. Conversely, the artist often finds himself repelled from using technical, scientific terms because of their "coldness" and incomprehensibility, yet his breadth of scope is unimpaired.

Neither works of art nor of science survive unchanged, but the changes come about in different ways. In science the intellectual product, equation, or invention continually undergoes an enrichment through the discovery and elaboration of new relationships. In Figure 3, this is expressed as a continual elaboration of constructs, connecting logical relationships (single lines) and operational recipes (double lines). Or the scientific work may suffer decay through the discovery of inherent errors. In either case, one has the impression on the whole of an orderly, rational process. The influences which change works of art are twofold: the mellowing, subduing, abrasive effect of time, and the cumulative interpretations of succeeding generations. But these interpretations are the result not of orderly elaboration but of insight governed largely by accident. Perhaps there is a kind of order to these insights, but if so, it is of a different kind.

DISCURSIVE SYMBOLISM-PRESENTATIONAL MEANS. In their tools for thinking and communicating, the sciences are restricted to the more austere type of discursive symbolism. The humanities do not recognize such a limitation. In their scientific writing, scientists tend to avoid the use of words with great connotational range. Humanists do not exclude any aids to communication. This difference in their tools leads to interesting differences in the kinds of results they achieve in their respective areas of knowledge and experience.

Except in pure mathematical discourse, it is practically impossible for the scientist to use language barren of connotational overtones. The English literary critic T. R. Henn has called attention to this in lectures originally written for presentation to a group of science students. He says:

> If you listen to the following passage, you will, I think, realize that a far greater number of words carry "images" than most of us realize. I will try to stress such words as I read.
>
> "*Suppose* that the pile were to be *started* by simultaneous *release* (in the uranium metal) of N high-energy neutrons. Most of these neutrons originally have energies above the *threshold* energy of fission of U-238. However, as the neutrons pass *back and forth* in the metal and moderator, they *suffer* numerous inelastic *collisions* with the uranium and numerous elastic *collisions* with the moderator, and all these collisions *serve* to *reduce* the energies below that *threshold*. Specifically, in a typical graphite-moderated pile a neutron that has *escaped* from the uranium into the graphite *travels* on the average about 2.5 cm. between collisions and makes on the average about 200 elastic collisions before passing from the graphite back into the uranium."
>
> In the original the word *average* is also italicized, presumably to carry emphasis.[17]

In writing designed for the non-scientist, words barren of all connotation would be worthless, for the reader would find such writing repulsive. On the other hand, the skillful artist can compress quantities of information into a few well-chosen words or phrases. Professor Alexander M. Witherspoon has called to my attention an example of such writing in a report by the newspaperman William L. Lawrence.

> Experiments at Cornell University have provided the last link in the chain of experimental evidence solving the mystery of the sun's apparently inexhaustible store of energy which keeps life on earth going.
>
> The final step in an astrophysical research conducted by Professor H. A. Bethe was reported today by him and Dr. M. G. Holloway, his collaborator at the closing session of the annual Washington meeting of the American Physical Society.
>
> According to the theory, the carbon in the sun constituted a veritable "cosmic Phoenix," forever being devoured in flames of hydrogen, and yet resurrecting itself in its full original state every 52,550,000 years, to start the cycle all over again. . . .[18]

Notice how many words and phrases in this report carry rich connotational references: "mystery," "life on earth," "cosmic Phoenix," "devoured," "resurrection." The mythological reference carries the idea to the reader by a powerful shorthand.

This is not to say that scientists try to exclude all connotational words from their writings. That would be impossible in the social and biological sciences, though it may be possible in the physical sciences. In the fantastic field of nuclear theory the scientists are concerned with matters so remote from everyday life that they can feel free of the implications of connotational meanings which in other fields clamp an ascetic rigor upon their language. Nuclear scientists can employ such terms as "magic numbers" in discussing theory or can use the word "barn" for the unit for nuclear cross section determined by bombardment with nuclear particles, playing on the notion of being able to hit "a red door in a green barn," which is well known to be a practically unmissable target.

The artist, always faced with the need for wider or more subtle expressions and for new ways of presenting his ideas and feelings, is not limited in his choice of words as is the scientist. If he works in a discursive medium, as do the poet, novelist, and dramatist, then he has at his disposal a great armory of weapons with which to capture the elusive—or he may contrive new weapons. Some of these are discussed by T. R. Henn.[19] There is the mystical symbolism of Blake:

O Rose, thou art sick!
The invisible worm,
That flies in the night,
In the howling storm,

Has found out thy bed
Of crimson joy;
And his dark secret love
Does thy life destroy.

There are mythological, historical, or legendary allusions, as used, for example, by Milton, writing of Satan reviewing the troops of hell:

And all who since, baptiz'd or infidel,
Jousted in Aspramont or Montalban,
Damasco, or Marocco, or Trebisond;
Or whom Biserta sent from Afric shore
When Charlemain with all his peerage fell
By Fontarabbia . . .

(Henn suggests that perhaps at some time the names of Dieppe or Anzio or Arnheim may one day find themselves in metrical form, for "the issues were perhaps greater than at Roncesvalles.")

The poet or novelist can make new words, "without running too much risk of becoming incomprehensible, by using double-epithets, as Keats did; by using more violently-yoked compounds as Hopkins did; or even by experimenting with a kind of new speech, relying on the sound-values of portions of known words, welded or fused together, like Gertrude Stein or James Joyce." Still another method, which in the hands of T. S. Eliot has yielded "complex results, obtainable in no other way" is that of resetting in a new context "words or phrases or lines *together with the meaning which surrounded them in their previous context,*" so that they interact with each other and produce new effects. And there are many other devices.

Both the artist and the scientist are trying to extend the power of their tools in any way they can. Just as the artist invents new words and reworks old phrases, so the scientist, in order to deal with ever more subtle constructs and connections, invents new tools—Newton invented the calculus, and, more recently, the physicist Werner Heisenberg invented the matrix calculus. Neither artist nor scientist limits himself to discursive or presentational symbolism, but the emphasis of each is different.

The differences in emphasis are inevitably limited by *means.* Both scientists and humanists tend to choose as research subjects those which they are equipped to study and to avoid those which they lack the means to handle. This tendency is illustrated by the fact that frequently some extremely expensive *instrument* dictates what studies are to be made ("we've got to use it because it costs so much"); and the investigators become the tools, doing problems to keep the instrument busy. The "equity" represented by an investment weighs more than the "equity" represented by the intelligence, and we have an example of the difficulty, noted by the engineer Charles F. Kettering, of taking account of ideas in a balance sheet. Perhaps this phenomenon can be justified in industry, but it is indefensible in the university Nevertheless, it still remains the reason for a good deal of "means-centered" research, when the needs of men demand "problem-centered" research. Here too we find a similarity between the humanities and the sciences.

THEORETICAL-ESTHETIC. The philosopher F. S. C. Northrop his discussed in some detail those two components of things of all kinds which, in their interactions with human beings, he designates as the theoretical and the esthetic components.[20] Whatever the thing may be, whether animate or inanimate, its esthetic component is the thing as immediately experienced and emotionally felt, the intuitively given, purely empirical, ineffable delivery of the senses. The theoretic component is the inferred, hypothetically postulated, and experimentally verified component of the thing (see Figure 3).

One feature distinguishing the sciences from the humanities, as I have pointed out, is the emphasis of the former on the theoretic component and of the latter on the esthetic. The theoretic is susceptible of logical manipulation and of a type of precise handling which to some extent makes it possible to control the things so treated. The esthetic yields, to some extent, to other kinds of handling. However, as I have shown, the distinction is not absolute and must be used with care. Many modern movements suggest a laying hold of the theoretic by the humanities and of the esthetic by the sciences. Professor Northrop has opened some attractive vistas through his use of theoretic and esthetic components as means for contrasting and uniting areas of knowledge and experience.

John Dewey has spoken of "the odd notion that an artist does not think and a scientific inquirer does nothing else,"[21] and he stresses that there is great similarity of method between the two but that it is in their data that the great differences occur.

> Only the psychology that has separated things which in reality belong together holds that scientists and philosophers think while poets and painters follow their feelings. . . . As I have already said, the only significant distinction concerns the kind of material to which emotionalized imagination adheres. Those who are called artists have as their subject matter the qualities of things of direct experience; "intellectual" enquirers deal with these qualities at one remove, through the medium of symbols that stand for qualities but are not significant in their immediate presence. The ultimate difference is enormous as far as the techniques of thought and emotion are concerned. But there is no difference as far as dependence on emotion-

> alized ideas and subconscious maturing are concerned. Thinking directly in terms of colors, tones, images, is a different operation technically from thinking in words. But only superstition will hold that, because the meanings of paintings and symphonies cannot be translated into words, or that of poetry into prose, therefore thought is monopolized by the latter.[22]

Another odd notion is that scientists stoop when they try to convey ideas to a layman in picturesque language. It is therefore comforting to read that the great physicist Clerk Maxwell held that "for the sake of persons of different types, scientific truth should be presented in different forms and should be regarded as equally scientific whether it appears in the robust form and vivid colouring of a physical illustration, or in the tenuity and paleness of a symbolic expression."[23] Both of these men, Dewey and Maxwell, are unifiers in their fields—that is, they are philosophers. Their attitudes are typical of the creative, synthetic approach.

CHAPTER 6

Results: II

Ratio-Analogy-Metaphor; General-Particular; Assent-Dissent; Repeatable-Unique.

RATIO-ANALOGY-METAPHOR. As I illustrated in the second chapter, a marked difference between science and art results from the difference in the tools that are used for communication. I wish now to draw this contrast more clearly and to show some underlying similarities.

The scientist continually drives himself to try to state mathematical relationships among his constructs. The mathematical expressions he uses are ratios or formulas of one kind or another. A ratio is a relationship which is logically ineluctable. Thus, if 2 is to 3 as 6 is to x, then by simple calculation, x *must* be 9. The relationship may be stated in various ways—$2:3::6:x$; or, $2/3=6/x$; or, $x=(3\times6)/2$. But x *must* represent 9 in this relationship. Such a mathematical proportionality must display a high degree of elegance to the person who grasps it for the first time. One mathematician has written that when, as a youth, he first came upon the ratio and realized its elegance, he became convinced of the power of mathematics.

But there are some constructs in science which cannot be, or at least have not yet been, related mathematically to each other. They can be related only by analogy, which functions as an imperfect ratio or proportionality. In the arts, where quantification is not usually a goal, analogy is even more important. But for the many experiences which the humanist must convey that are so elusive they are almost incommunicable, analogy may be too crude a tool, and the artist must invoke the magic of metaphor. One contrast between the sciences and humanities, then, is that the former most commonly use ratio and analogy as tools for communication while the latter use chiefly analogy and metaphor. These distinctions can be illustrated by means of a few examples.

Most great physical generalizations are stated in mathematical terms. Newton's law about gravitation, presented at the beginning of Chapter 2, is one of these. All such mathematical equations are ratios. Some are tightly stated, like the $\mathbf{F}=G(m_1m_2)/s^2$, which contains one constant of proportionality. Such an equation leaves little room for conflicting interpretations once the symbols have been defined. Others are less tightly drawn, and some are flexible. These latter equations may have been made to fit their data by the use of several adjustable parameters. If they are used as the basis of theoretical interpretations, it can happen that to describe the same set of data two scientists will use two different equations and arrive at two different theories. Such situations have led to some harsh polemics. An elastic equation which can be made to fit a set of data does not prove the underlying theory on which it is based. If it contains many adjustable parameters it verges upon analogy. For this reason scientists seek simple equations, preferably ones in which the constants present serve only to fit the units together. When alternative interpretations of data are presented the methods of scientific validation usually insure an eventual choice of the more correct interpretation and the more correct use of ratios and analogies.

The development of the use of number ratios in describing phenomena has a long history. There is a legend that Pythagoras, who flourished in the sixth century B.C., discovered through systematic experiments with stringed instruments that a given string produces pleasing sounds harmoniously related to each other when the string is stopped at such points along its length that the values for the lengths of the vibrating parts form simple numerical ratios.[1] Thus, if one of two strings of equal length tuned to the same note is stopped at three quarters of its length, the two sounded together make a pleasing harmony. Another pleasing effect is produced by the two strings if one is stopped at the two-thirds point, and again at the halfway point. Taking the unstopped string as unit length (1) these relations are 1:3/4:-2/3:1/2. Or, converting to whole number relations, 12:9:8:6 (12/12:9/12:8/12:6/12). The ratios of 12:9, 12:8, and 12:6 are our fourth, fifth, and octave.

Pythagoras' discovery is remarkable when we realize that he had no written number system like ours, but worked with pebbles and marks in the sand. Imagine his pleasure and excitement on realizing that he had discovered an essential order underlying an aesthetic experience! He found a connection between an ordered set of numbers and a pleasurable experience, between mathematics and aesthetics. In his time such a connection was taken to imply something about the universe, just as the pleasurable experience of musical harmony carried with it an analogy to a greater harmony in the world. This was strengthened by further studies in which other harmonies were found.

For example, looking again at the ratio 12:8:6, we can see that 8 holds an interesting relation to the other two numbers. Pythagoras observed that "by whatever part of itself the first number exceeds the second, the second exceeds the third by the same part of the third." A number in such a relationship he called an "harmonic mean." The first (12) exceeds the second (8) by 4/12, and the second exceeds the third by 2/6, whence 8 is the harmonic mean because 4/12=2/6. By extending the concept of the harmonic mean to geometry, (a cube, which has 12 edges, 8 angles, and 6 faces came to be called a "geometric harmony") Pythagoras thus related, in principle, geometry to aesthetics.

When we realize that the human ear is sensitive to small differences in the wavelengths of sounds and think of the complicated fractions which can represent pleasant or unpleasant sounds, it becomes apparent that a tremendous amount of number juggling can be done with relations of these kinds. And, in fact, Pythagoras and his students did indulge in a great deal of this entrancing exercise. Harmonic proportions—and many other kinds of proportions, such as arithmetic and geometric, with their associated "means"—came to be found more and more frequently in natural phenomena, and there was an understandably strong tendency, under the drive of this great idea, to force the issue. Where these signs of order could not be found, it was a short step to the conclusion that the phenomena were at fault. (This is a characteristic of ideological systems even today.)

Similar connections were made between number ratios and pleasing shapes in ancient times, as Jay Hambridge has shown from an analysis of Greek architecture, sculpture, and vase shapes[2] (see Figure 11, page 94.); and great excitement and deep pleasure attended the discoveries of such connections as these. It took a great leap of the imagination to argue that the harmony of strings, which connected number ratios with aesthetic satisfactions, was but one manifestation of a greater harmony. Pythagoras felt that the proper way to interpret *all* phenomena was through numerical laws; he believed there was a harmony underlying *all* phenomena and that the task of scholars was to find it. By his synthetic activity, he connected the art and science of his day.

The relation between harmony and numbers was extended by analogy to philosophy and religion. Indeed, Pythagoras is reputed to have said that analogy lies at the root of all that is most beautiful. And since analogy is a tool for creative work in science and art, Pythagoras is right. Practically all scientific research is initiated through analogy, and the same may be said for the arts. As soon as synthesis begins, analogy plays a determinative role—as in the activity of classification. Analogy leads the way to new insights, provided only that the analogy is inexact or broad enough. For an exact analogy is an identity and conveys nothing new. An analogy guides through its imperfections; yet it must not be so far-fetched that it makes no connections. To invoke analogy is a recognized step in the solution of scientific problems.

The value of metaphor and analogy is marked in the arts.

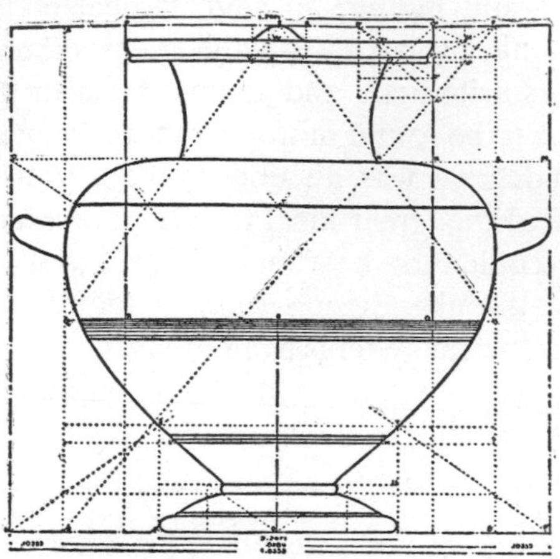

Figure 11. Black figured Hydria (measured and drawn by L. D. Caskey). From Jay Hambidge, *Dynamic Symmetry: The Greek Vase* (Yale University Press, 1920), Figure 16. According to the author, the plan of this vase is "a theme in root-two." A rectangle drawn on the width and total height (AFBO) is divided at the top of the set of parallel lines near the middle of the vase (CJ) into two parts. The lower part is divisible into two equal squares (CEDO and EJBD). The upper is of such a size that the ratio of its side (AF), the width of the vase, to its end (AC), the height from the upper of the parallel lines to the top of the vase, has the value $\sqrt{2}$. That there is an order and symmetry here is evident. How far the geometrical analysis can be pushed is another matter.

When the data are so complex or subjective that they defy logical discursive symbolism, then discourse turns to metaphor and analogy, verbal or presentational. This is particularly so in religion, where analogy and metaphor have served expression and analogy has served investigation.

The essence of analogy and metaphor is that they do not deal with identities but with relations of likeness. In a sense, an analogy or metaphor is a kind of model, which may be verbalized or pictured in some way or acted out. The Zuñi Indians communicate with their gods by acting out metaphors. "In the priests' retreats for rain they roll round stones across the floor to produce thunder, water is sprinkled to cause rain, a bowl of water is placed upon the altar that the springs may be full, suds are beaten up from a native plant that clouds may pile in the heavens, tobacco smoke is blown out that the gods 'may not withhold their misty breath.' "[3] In using analogy (and simile and metaphor) the scientist may not abandon logic and the experimental method in favor of fantasy. But to the artist no device for making the incommunicable communicable can be prohibited.

GENERAL-PARTICULAR. The sciences and the arts are often compared in terms of their preoccupation with the general and the particular—a distinction related to that between the objective and the subjective. The comparison exposes the roots of some persistent problems.

Science does indeed aim toward the general statement, but the scientist never forgets the individual fact, the source of his data. He is interested in the individual fact, though not in its individuality. From the belief that science deals only with the general it is an easy step to the belief that science is infallible. If one reasons from a general scientific statement (a premise) to a conclusion by correct logical deduction, and if the premise is true, then it follows that the conclusion is infallibly true. But logical deduction cannot introduce any new and independent result; it simply connects a general statement (the premise) with a conclusion implied by the premise.[4] But the premise itself, if it is a scientific one, was derived, at least indirectly, from particular facts by a process of induction—a process by no means infallible. A given set of facts suggests many constructs, or generalizations, some of which are true, some false. And even if the generalization as a construct is taken to be exact, fallibility and tentativeness enter into its connection with the individual fact through the medium of the operational and other correlations (Figure 3).

It is, indeed, the objective of science to develop ever more widely applicable and, at the same time, ever more precise generalizations—that is, to develop an ever more deductive science. But as long as the appeal to fact is recognized as a critical part of the procedure by which the generalizations are verified, science cannot renounce the individual subjects. Without the appeal to individual facts there can be no science.

The scientific generalization is an expression of a different "reality"—a reality abstracted from the individual occurrence—from the "reality" with which the descriptive historian or artist is concerned—the "reality" of the individual. The artist is engaged in a kind of (analytic) search for reality which seeks the qualities of the individual that make it individual. This was discussed, to some extent, in the section of the previous chapter on qualitative precision.

There is a connection between this contrast of the general and the particular and that of the objective and the subjective. For where either objectiveness or generalization is sought, abstraction from the individual datum and elimination of the characteristics that give the observer his uniqueness both seem necessary. Knowledge of what gives the individual datum individuality or particularity seems often to involve a strong subjective component. Again, the connection between the objective and the general and between the subjective and the particular becomes apparent if it is asked how true objective and subjective observations are. Irwin Edman suggests an answer:

> For myself, I think there is only confusion to be found in using the same term for truth experimentally and demonstrably verifiable and the sense of urgent and persuasive meaning and value in the arts. The poets and the prophets use images suggestive poignantly of things and ideas deeply cherishable not least because of the mode of their expression. But whether truth is a characteristic of works of art or not, the fact is that works of art do convey meanings so effectively that they are held to reveal truth. Such effects raise the whole question of the relation of image to literal statement, of myth to truth. The name "truth" perhaps should be rescued for propositions, but we need perhaps a new term, "authenticity" or "revelation," to identify that felt ultimacy, that irrefutable quality which is experience in art, in love, and in religion. The arts suggest at least that something supplementary to

scientific truth is present in the arts, something that requires another and less literal name.[5]

I shall present, in the next two chapters, a definition of truth that reconciles these, even though (at least in the more extreme contrasts between art and science) two different kinds of truth—truth-about and truth-to, as John Hospers calls them—seem to be communicated.

As we found before, much of the difference between art and science derives from the difference in their methods of expression. Science expresses generality by devising abstract, and thus general, constructs; art does so by presenting a particular composed of the most general attributes. This is a likely outcome of their different emphases: the emphasis of science is on ideas; of the arts, on feelings and emotions. To communicate ideas, abstract discursive and presentational symbols serve. But to communicate feeling, concreteness is necessary. Even the greatest abstractions (e.g. God) must be translated to lower abstraction levels in order to gain concreteness—but not to too low a level of abstraction: "Thou shalt not make unto thee any graven image." A "true" painting or poem or proverb is one which epitomizes the general as succinctly and simply as does a true statement of natural law in science (Figs. 12, 13, pp. 102-103). Here, indeed, is a contrast between the sciences and the arts: *Science deals with the general in general terms; art through a concrete example.* But art tends also to universal principles, and its exclusive preoccupation with the individual is only apparent. Thus, as Haskell points out, in Greek tragedy the individual character works out decrees of the gods: *general principles.*[6] These very principles were later formulated *by* science (psychology) and actually given the names of the characters in Greek drama, e.g. Oedipus, Electra.

This strong and healthy preoccupation of the arts with general principles has been obscured by certain modern schools which, in pursuing principles of arbitrariness and senselessness, try deliberately to avoid portrayal of general principles. However, in so doing, they set forth meaninglessness as a general principle —a principle expounded as such by certain branches of existentialism. In a time of breakdown, they display breakdown as a universal. In general, we may conclude that the more universal and integrative the principles, emotions, attitudes, and moods displayed by a work of art, the greater it is esteemed during periods of integrated civilization. The opposite holds during periods of cultural breakdown. The successful artist, poets, painters, dramatists, novelists in any given age are those in whose works people recognize themselves and their milieu most forcefully and in the ways they like best, or, in any event, feel most keenly.

Because of the imprecision of the terms used in expressing the truths of the arts, continues Haskell, these truths cannot be compiled into powerful systems. Hence, the Age of Science transforms the globe while the Ages of Art come and go with nothing like the impact of the former. However, in the Age of Science it will be the arts and integrated, unified, science together, or else the arts and ideologies together, that will determine the direction of the transforming force of science. *Hence, it is the responsibility of all intelligent people, and of constructive forces embodied in such institutions as colleges, universities, and churches, to resist the prevailing spirit during a period of cultural breakdown and not be overborne by it.* Theirs is the high privilege of working together to repair and rebuild.

ASSENT-DISSENT. For the sake of showing similarities between science and art, and for the purpose of exposing some possible misunderstandings, we must compare the artist's and scientist's assent to or dissent from "authority."

The best of modern scientists feel a vocation, a mission. They want further understanding of the world and everything in it. They are engaged in works that have meaning and use. Their aim is to be lucid within the limitations of their terminology, and when they sign their work it is not only for personal satisfaction but also to guarantee the work. They have a universal language—in the physical sciences, mathematics—and standards of probity, restraint, and integrity which are widely accepted and which are maintained through the operation of the public aspect of scientific objectivity. There is thus a unanimity among scientists. It would be as wrong to imagine that this unanimity is imposed by an exterior authority as to suppose that it is easily obtained. The training of the scientist leads him to assent to the objective tests for validity and the criteria of truthfulness which other scientists must apply to his work. He is free within the framework of these requirements to dissent from the opinions of others and from any attempts to injure the structure of science, whether inadvertent or intentional. As a scientist, he is accountable for his work only in that it be good science. The authority to which he ultimately assents is that authority within himself which requires him, as a human being, to be rational.

Much the same can be said for the artist. But his situation is complicated by the lack of widely accepted criteria for the validity and, hence, worth of his work. At various times in history there seems to have been a unanimity underlying traditional art, whether Christian or Oriental, in the sense that the ideas expressed by artists were determined by traditional doctrine. If the artist, because of his training, assented freely to traditional doctrine he could execute his works with originality, in his own style, as "an unconscious self-expression of the free man,"[7] while remaining within a framework which might not change much for a thousand years—a framework unified by the principles of traditional Christian and Oriental philosophies. The traditional artists who accepted these philosophies must have felt themselves to be so imbued with the philosophy of the age that in interpreting it they could as artists remain free. Part of the function of art in such periods was to express meaning of a generally accepted kind. Concomitantly, there could develop generally accepted canons of style which allowed some test of the quality of a work of art.

Just as traditional artists have been free, so the thoroughgoing Communist, Fascist, or Nazi, having conformed to the doctrine, must feel himself to be a free agent. But in the first of these he has conformed to a doctrine based on a partial and incorrect appraisal of the world which, claiming the validity of empirical fact and thus being incorrigible, leaves him free to be fundamentally in error. In the next two, he has conformed to doctrines based on insane appraisals of the world. But, as one writer put it during the growth of nazism, "when everyone is in a straight-jacket, it is not so noticeable." Though art produced by these movements may conform to some stylistic standards, they are not widely accepted or valid.

The arts today have broken away from tradition and cannot easily be judged by traditional standards. The artist is required to express his vision, and he casts about for new modes of expression. This must always be a difficult enterprise, since it involves the creation of new symbolic transformations. Perhaps the turbulence and confusion of much modern art is a necessary concomitant of this venture. Criteria of validity are hard come by, and the difficulty of separating the good from the bad is increased. The difficulty is further complicated by the contemporary cults of personality and of personal expression,[8] of irrationality, of anti-intellectualism, and of meaninglessness, which are hailed by many people as "speaking to their condition." But it is a sick condition they speak to, symptomatic of an era of cultural breakdown. These cults reflect an excess of analytic emphasis, which is part of the syndrome. For analysis *by itself*—the reporting of facts, "realism," the collection of instances—bears little meaning no matter how well done. If analysis is taken to be all there is, then these cults of meaninglessness can easily draw their deluded adherents. With the battle cry of "dissent," many of them advocate, tragically, dissent from the authority (and responsibility) within all of us to be rational human beings.[9]

I do not wish to imply that it would be desirable to seek some goal of absolute rationality. There are many kinds of irrationality which are of the greatest value to humanity. But it takes the rational to recognize the irrational, and not the other way around.[10] Here, we see one of those rare one-way relationships that can be utilized to support judgment. The human race has struggled for millennia to increase the rational component in man's behavior. This is a continuing battle, and a noble one, and one intimately related to the battle for life which is fought against the degenerative forces of inanimate nature. A system left to itself will inevitably degrade. Only constant vigilance combined with constant effort can keep us culturally alive. In the long run, we never get something for nothing.

It is only when we see the activities of analysis, synthesis, and reduction to practice functioning well together that we see a whole system. Such a system defines the criteria which I have invoked to test great art (and science). Many modern humanists adhere to the highest concepts of art—such concepts as that the purpose of the arts lies beyond the individual artist, that unless the artist is constructive, helping us to rise above ourselves and giving us new insights and new dignity, his works cannot be certified as great. Emphasis on analysis tends to emphasize the secular. Emphasis on complete systems tends to reveal the sacramental nature of life.

Neither science nor art can be censured for the failings of individual scientists and artists. Anything that has been made or discovered or invented may be used for good or evil. This is the way things go: the good, the constructive, is always hard come by; evil is easy. The living being is always fighting death; the human spirit, in a healthy culture, always opposes the degenerative trend that in physical chemistry is summed up in the second law of thermodynamics. Creative artists and scientists take the hard, fatiguing way of assent to the requirements of life; the weak, sick, or perverse in both camps dissent from life and let decay and death take over.

REPEATABLE AND GENERAL-UNIQUE AND INDIVIDUAL. The movement of all science is from the correlational toward the theoretical. Information about individuals, whether animate beings or inanimate data, must be collected; and in this respect the scientist is deeply concerned with the individual (as I have said in the section "General-Particular"), but only as a starting point. This is an early stage in scientific activity. It is followed, according to the Baconian approach to scientific problems, by classification and a search for patterns. At this point, one has already left the individual far behind. Perception itself begins the process of abstraction, for no perception is as rich as what is perceived—there are always other ways of looking. When theory is established, the character of the individual is lost. The search for patterns in data, for similarities in behavior, is always a search for the more general and always submerges the individual.[11]

As one moves along the continuum of Figure 1 toward the side of the arts, emphasis upon the individual increases, but for the purpose of epitomizing the general. In *Rasselas* Samuel Johnson wrote:

> The business of a poet . . . is to examine, not the individual, but the species; to remark general properties and large appearances. He does not number the streaks of the tulip, or describe the different shades of the verdure of the forest. He is to exhibit in his portraits of nature such prominent and striking features as recall the original to every mind, and must neglect the minuter discriminations, which one may have remarked, and another have neglected, for those characteristics which are alike obvious to vigilance and carelessness. But the knowledge of nature is only half the task of the poet; he must be acquainted likewise with all the modes of life. His character requires that he estimate the happiness and misery of every condition, observe the power of all the passions in all their combinations, and trace the changes of the human mind as they are modified by various institutions and accidental influences of climate or custom, from the sprightliness of infancy to the despondence of decrepitude . . .[12]

The critic shows in this passage that he recognizes the proper function and limits of analysis ("he does not number the streaks of the tulip"), of synthesis ("remark general properties" and "trace the changes"), and of reduction to practice ("recall the original to every mind") in the poet's business. In this way, the general is communicated so as to recall the individual. Even in

Figure 12. Auguste Rodin, "The Kiss." Marble, 1886, The Rodin Museum, Paris. © by S.P.A.D.E.M.—Paris.

Figure 13. Auguste Rodin, "The Hand of God." Marble, 1897-1898, The Rodin Museum, Paris. © by S.P.A.D.E.M.—Paris. ". . . it is simply the power of character that makes beauty in art." (*Rodin and His Work,* Phaidon Press, London. The quotation is from a statement attributed to Rodin.)

Figure 14. Constantin Brancusi, "Bird." Marble, 1912, the Arensberg Collection, Philadelphia Museum of Art. (From Christian Zervos, *Constantin Brancusi,* Cahiers d'Art edition, Paris, 1957.)

Figure 15. Constantin Brancusi, "The Newborn." Marble, 1915, Arensberg Collection, Philadelphia Museum of Art. (From Christian Zervos, *Constantin Brancusi,* Cahiers d'Art edition, Paris, 1957.)

the act of perception some of the character of the individual is lost. The artist, in trying to see better, must by some contrivance of genius surmount this difficulty. When the critic Konrad Fiedler said "that the aim of painting is to furnish a fuller and completer view of things than can be obtained in the ordinary intercourse with them,"[13] he was noting that the presentation of general attributes in concrete form is characteristic of great art (see Figures 14 and 15, between pages 102-103).

Ortega describes a current movement in art which, while claiming to seek the quintessence of individuality, in a sense departs from the individual. It represents an extreme branch of existentialism and is part of the cult of meaninglessness. Ortega describes the movement as a dehumanization—a disencumbering of the art (painting, music, poetry) of its human matter. To achieve such an objective and still make sense must be difficult, if not impossible.

The term "individual" can be used in two senses. The theoretical sciences comprise knowledge derived from data about individual phenomena, but exclude the particular factors that make the individual phenomenon unique, that give it its individuality. The humanities do not exclude these factors. When particular factors and variations are taken into account in statistical studies, it is only with a view to grouping them. On the other hand, the particulars that are used by the arts are *representative* particulars which, for artist and audience, state generalities.

CHAPTER 7

Relative-Absolute

After bowling along a parkway at sixty miles per hour, how unbearably slow the twenty-five mile limit through town seems. Yet this can seem desirably fast when thick traffic slows us down to ten. "It's all relative," we say. We mean it is relative to our frames of reference, which are in this case our inner and outer environments. We may even feel soothed by the thought that "after all, science says everything is relative, doesn't it?"

Science never says anything, of course. But the interpretation may legitimately be made, if properly qualified, that in science the relativity of many phenomena is noticeable. The theory of relativity is commonly invoked to support this interpretation in realms far beyond those to which the theory applies. Indeed, the term "relativity" has acquired such status that it is used to support such monstrous theories as that of "cultural relativity," which could not possibly receive any sanction from the physical theories of Einstein. But the worst misuse of this concept of the relativity of many things arises when, by some peculiar perversion, the great prestige of science is invoked through the theory of relativity to support the idea that absolutes are meaningless and we have no further need for them. This myth has done incalculable harm. It has led scientists themselves into absurdities. It has instigated a host of cults of the meaningless, the chaotic, and the irrational. Many humanists who would know better if they knew some science (for humanists are traditionally concerned with wholes and absolutes) have been frightened into imitation of "science," submissive impotence, or irrational attack on "science." The scientist, in investigating the world, is impressed by the inescapable relativity of things. In this impression he finds companionship with his colleagues in the arts. And they *both* find a need for absolutes, but of different kinds.

The scientist uses the term "absolute" as an adjective to characterize three kinds of things: one, an instrumentally defined quantity; two, a mathematically defined quantity; and three, a philosophically defined position. These can be explained through examples.

The metric—or c.g.s. (centimeter-gram-second)—system is used universally in scientific circles as a standard of measurement. In technical practice in the United States and in England the f.p.s. (foot-pound-second) system is used generally, and there are some other systems which are only locally important. In any system, the unit of length is fundamental to all other measurements, since other measurements, such as volume, time, temperature, can be derived from it, in conjunction with the properties of chemically pure substances. The thing that constitutes the primary standard of length in the c.g.s. system is kept at the International Bureau of Weights and Measures at Sèvres, near Paris. It consists of a rod of platinum-iridium alloy, with a special X-like cross section, designed for maximum rigidity, on which are ruled two very fine lines. The distance between these two lines, when the rod is at 0° centigrade, is defined as one meter. (The primary standard of the f.p.s. system, the absolute yard, is defined in a similar way, as the distance between two lines on a similar unit kept at the National Physics Laboratory, Teddington, near London.) This absolute meter, *The Meter*, is used as a primary standard to calibrate secondary and tertiary standards which are then used as working standards for calibrations of other measuring instruments like rulers. Now, an important feature of this absolute standard is that it was *defined*. (The fact that it was related to a "natural" constant, being considered to be 1/40,000,000 of the circumference of the earth, does not change the arbitrary nature of the definition, nor does the modern tendency to make some of the units more precise by relating them to atomic phenomena.) The standard was set up in order to have an absolute against which to test unknowns. It provided an acknowledged legal standard.

This kind of absolute standard makes the scientist a little uneasy. He would like to reduce it to something more fundamental, something less arbitrary. Without removing entirely the arbitrary nature of the measurement, the term "absolute" is used in a second sense, which some scientists feel to be somewhat more satisfactory, though it is closely related to the first sense of the term. It is used to characterize a mathematically defined limit. It is in this sense that the scientist speaks of absolute zero or the absolute scale of temperature, based upon absolute zero. The concept is not a difficult one to grasp, though, like all great achievements, it was hard to come by.

If one tries to measure the temperature of different objects with the hand, one can say only that this object feels colder or warmer than that one under given circumstances. The most quantitative statement possible is that one object feels "much warmer" or "slightly warmer" than another. However, one can compare with each other simultaneous changes or differences of different kinds, such as the change in length of a rod or of a column of a liquid as it is warmed. When a liquid such as alcohol or mercury is heated it expands, that is to say, its *volume* increases. If the liquid is enclosed in a bulb and tube, as in an ordinary thermometer, the increase in volume with heating can manifest itself as a lengthening of the column of the liquid in the tube or stem of the thermometer, the bulb being always full, and an empty space being provided above the column in the stem of the thermometer. Using this device, and interpreting what it shows by means of the observation that an increase in heat causes an increase in length in the column of liquid in the stem of the thermometer, it is possible always to tell which of two bodies is hotter, because when the thermometer is brought in turn to the temperature of each (when it is put into effective contact with the body and kept there until there is no change in the length of the column of mercury) the column of mercury will be longer with the hotter body. This is still not much better than using a hand, for one still does not know how much hotter one body is than the other. However, it is vastly superior to comparing the results obtained by *different* hands.

To obtain a quantitative statement about the temperature one has to calibrate the thermometer. This was done conveniently in the early days of thermometry by using as the calibration points the freezing point of water (at atmospheric pressure, and saturated with air in a normal manner) and the boiling point of water, again at atmospheric pressure. The procedure was to immerse the thermometer in ice and water. When the end of the column of mercury came to rest, indicating that the whole thermometer was at the same temperature as the liquid, this "fixed point" was marked on the stem of the thermometer. The thermometer was then allowed to warm up and eventually was immersed in actively boiling water at one atmosphere; and, after the end of the column of expanding mercury had stopped moving, another fixed point was marked on the stem. There were thus two marks on the thermometer stem. The scientist Celsius arbitrarily designated the freezing point as zero and the boiling point as 100. The distance from zero to 100 was then divided into equal divisions which are called degrees. It is assumed that the volume expansion of mercury is uniform and that the changes in size of bulb and tube on heating are compensated. The arbitrariness of this procedure is much like that in defining the meter or the foot. It is equally obvious here because there are three thermometer scales in use—with three different kinds of degrees all expressed by the same symbol. The freezing point of water, which is zero degrees on the centigrade scale (0°C), is 32 degrees on the Fahrenheit scale (32°F); and zero degrees on the Reaumur scale (0°R); similarly, the boiling point of water is 100°C, 212°F, and 80°R.

Obviously, the "degrees" are different. Most theoretical scientists agreed to standardize on the centigrade kind of degree (c.g.s. system), but there still remained the arbitrary zero designation, using ice and water as the fixed point. Since it was known that things colder than ice and water could be experienced —winter weather in northern countries or on high mountains— the degree marks on the thermometer were extended below zero degrees and called minus, or negative. As knowledge of physics and chemistry grew it became apparent that there is a lower "limit" of temperature, which may be approached by the progressive removal of heat from objects. The physicist Lord Kelvin was able to formulate this limit mathematically and to show how it could be derived by calculation. One might say that as one abstracts heat energy from a substance the less there is left of it, and the more difficult it becomes to abstract the remaining heat energy. By drawing a mathematical graph of the process of removing heat from an object, one can predict mathematically that if all the heat were removed and the temperature measured, it would read minus 273.16°C, that is 273.16°C below 0°C. This "is" the absolute zero, or zero degrees Kelvin (0°K). On the Kelvin scale all temperatures are positive numbers: water freezes at 273.16°K and boils at 373.16°K. There is nothing more "cold" than the absolute zero.

But absolute zero has never been reached, and for instrumental reasons (which are also philosophical and metaphysical) it can be predicted that absolute zero can never be reached. Yet it has a value which is as accurate, specific, and certain as any value *derived from measurements* in physics and chemistry. It is one of Margenau's constructs. The figures for the absolute zero on the Fahrenheit scale and on the Reaumur scale will, of course, be different from that on the centigrade scale. This is because the intervals between the degrees on the scales are different—that is to say, a different number of degrees is marked off between any two fixed points on one scale than on another. It is not the actual number given to the temperature measured on an absolute scale which is important to us but the fact that there is such a limit on the temperature scale. Still, the *value* of the absolute zero is just as uncertain as the uncertainty of the measurements used in designing it. Actually, the value has had to be changed slightly over the years.

Absolute zero is related by definition to certain ideal substances, for example, to the ideal gas. The concept of an ideal gas or an ideal solution or the other ideals which are used in physics and chemistry is in itself the concept of an absolute. It is not uncertain; it is something which is, in a sense, mathematically absolute. As Poincaré pointed out, it is perfectly general, perfectly precise, and of absolute certainty, this characteristic having been bestowed, so to speak voluntarily, by looking upon the definition as a convention.[1] It is a philosophical absolute, our third type.

By "philosophical absolute" I mean an imaginable or calculable ultimate or limit set up for the purpose of defining a category or of functioning as a reference point upon which to anchor the conceptual instruments used to examine reality. There are many of these absolutes. They last as long as they are useful (perhaps somewhat longer), and they are always subject to replacement as our concepts are refined. It is abstractions of a low level that are relative.

The absolute zero would be taken as a fiction by a strict instrumentalist who believes only what he can read on a dial. But the scientist unblushingly uses the concept of an absolute he can only predict and never actually reach, or else uses the concept of an absolute which derives its definition or its certainty from convention. Before inquiring into the reason why such scientific absolutes are considered necessary, we must consider how the term is used by the non-scientist.

Henri Focillon, speaking of style in art, observes:

> This term has two very different, indeed two opposite meanings. Style is an absolute. A style is a variable. The word "style" in its generic sense indicates a special and superior quality in a work of art; the quality, the peculiarly external value, that allows it to escape the bondage of time. Conceived as an absolute, style is not only a model, but also something whose validity is changeless. It is like a great summit that, rising between two slopes, sharply

> defines the expanse of skyline. In utilizing style as an absolute, we give expression to a very fundamental need: that of beholding ourselves in our widest possible intelligibility, in our most stable, our most universal aspect, beyond the fluctuations of history, beyond local and specific limitations. A style, on the other hand, is a development, a coherent grouping of forms united by a reciprocal fitness, whose essential harmony is nevertheless in many ways testing itself, building itself, and annihilating itself.[2]

There is a certain similarity of this usage to the scientific usage. Focillon is referring to what I would call diverse levels of abstraction. That aspect of style by which it transcends local value systems (local in space and time) lies on a high level of abstraction (Focillon even speaks of "a great summit . . . rising . . ."). The other aspect of style is the local, and hence low, level, and is relative. (Parenthetically, a survey and a statistical summary of local works would be unlikely to yield the absolute style. But then neither does it in physics. An intellectual intervention is needed, a topic to which I shall revert in a later chapter.)

The theologian seems to use the term "absolute" in still a different way. For him it expresses something to which a human being responds in recognition of an element both other than and within himself in the activity by which he seeks to apprehend the world. This is a transcendant something, of which he has no direct apprehension, but which he may conceive indirectly. Dorothy Emmett says:

> We know that we are inescapably related to something which vitally concerns us, and yet we have no direct apprehension of its intrinsic nature. Allied to this is the consciousness of finiteness; of the limited, fragmentary, transitory, character of man's life and knowledge. In contrast to this he responds with deep feeling to the thought of the Absolute, the Unconditioned, the Perfect, the Unchanging. He is also conscious of obligation, coming from he does not fully know where; is it society, his own mind,

> or some Law or Word beyond these? In any case, it is something which imposes judgment and discipline on his desires and appetites.[3]

When we allow for differences in language and degree of articulation we notice some similarity between the theological and scientific usages of "absolute." The absolute that belongs to religion, being on a high level of abstraction, is inarticulable to most men, but not unfeelable or unsensable. It is both other than and within man. Again we see the distinction between levels of abstraction, the distinction of the low level—local, "limited, fragmentary, transitory," that is, relative—from the high level, "the Unconditioned, the Perfect, the Unchanging," the Absolute. Again we recognize how the humanist, driving himself to communicate that which is inarticulable, turns to metaphor, that "tool for creation which God forgot inside one of His creatures when He made him."

"The divine spark" is no mere poetic phrase. It is one name for a quality that sets men above animals. Because of the great diversity of humankind, there are some men, even within smaller groupings, as in a city, who act as if they were merely animals. Yet the observer sees also those who are constructively and creatively human, and in agreement with the poet, historian, and philosopher he weighs heavily the positive, creative, constructive manifestations against the aparently inert, uncreative magma from which they must have sprung. Among the differences which set men above animals, the ability *to abstract*—to discriminate, to form constructs, to develop theories—is of the essence. Man seems continually to be reaching toward something "above" the individual, testifying to an urge which reflects a fundamental need.

The manifestations of this need are diverse, showing themselves in some form of worship—worship of the planets or of animals, of supposed ancestors of various kinds, of mythological creatures, of oneself, of the State (which usually boils down to the worship of a man living or recently living), of an hierarchy of gods and devils, of a single God—in short, of an Absolute.

Mankind shows a spiritual need for the absolute. And if the old absolutes are taken away a vacuum results into which rush new, or at least other, claimants for that exalted space.

The spiritual need for absolutes has often been recognized. Dilthey held that the yearning towards the absolute is an essential function of man's mind. Even though he knows he cannot reach it, he goes on imagining it. The systems so formed are "visions of the world," "images or ideas of the universe." It is recognized in the passage quoted from Dorothy Emmit above. It is acknowledged by the physicist von Weizsäcker when he remarks that "the suffering of every man from time and mutability is in fact so great that he must believe in something exempt from annihilation in order to be able to live . . ."[4] Another example of this idea may be seen in Eddington's remark about scientific explanation. He says that its endeavor to find identities in apparent differences "expresses a very elementary and instinctive habit of thought, which has unconsciously directed the course of scientific development. Briefly, it is the habit of thought which regards variety always as a challenge to further analysis; so that the *ultimate* end-product of analysis can only be sameness."[5] But this implies the Absolute. In each case, we find the relation of lower-level relatives resolved through the operation of absolutes of high levels of abstraction. They are resolved if understood; otherwise they are set in opposition.

As long as one looks at the structures, or static appearances, of the things one wishes to compare, it is difficult to see more than superficial similarities and differences among them. For a really penetrating insight, one has to examine their *functions*. There is no apparent resemblance between absolute zero, style as an absolute, and the absolute God. But when we ask ourselves what are the functions of these absolutes, a real clarification is possible.[6] For the absolute functions in response to a need. In every case, the function is appropriate to the need, even though the needs are different. Indeed, the needs are not comparable, and the kinds of absolutes are not comparable, but the functions are analogous.

Absolutes function in science as "base lines" from which the human activity of classifying and measuring can begin and be meaningfully communicated. They function in the arts as canons of style or beauty against which works of art can be measured. The canons of behavior, partaking of moral qualities, to which teachers, scientists, physicians, and others subscribe and against which their actual performance may be tested by their colleagues function as absolutes, as do, to a more qualified degree, the "codes of ethics" of business, professional, and other organizations. In the spiritual and moral realm, the absolute Good and the absolute Bad function as touchstones against which to try the quality of mundane achievement. The philosopher Coomaraswamy speaks of the similarity between Gothic (Scholastic) and early Indian ways of thinking about the Absolute, which comprises Beauty when taken from the point of view of aesthetics; Perfection, from that of ethics; and Truth, from the standpoint of the theory of knowledge. The relative factors, which are means of apprehension of these manifestations of the Absolute, are art, ethics, and science, respectively. Each of these is an utterance of the Absolute in terms of light *and* shade; good *and* evil; thesis *and* antithesis.[7]

The term "absolute" means different things in these different contexts, but the *functions* show much similarity. The need for an absolute is a concomitant of every act of valuation. But in science the absolute has as its sole function the provision of a base line or starting point—science uses, so to speak, a monofunctional absolute. In the moral and spiritual realm, however, the needs that are met by absolutes are as numerous, subtle, and exigent as we can conceive.

CHAPTER 8

Complete Statements, Whole Systems, Values

The need for an absolute is the concomitant of every act of valuation. As we have seen, the sciences as well as the arts have their absolutes. Science and art are both universal in scope, but neither is universal in emphasis. I have so far dealt chiefly with the separate emphases. But to see the whole we must combine the two. When we do, values emerge; and ethics, which is the "science" of valuing, emerges with them.

Ethics contains not only relative, lower level concepts but also unifying absolutes. Ethics is not simply a collection of particular facts, such as might be found through an empirical, descriptive investigation of morals, customs, or social practices. That is the *analytic* aspect only. If ethics is, in Professor Peter Carmichael's words, the rationale of ideas of virtue, beauty, self, good, and the vocation of life,[1] the other requirements which I have stressed—namely, synthesis and reduction to practice—must be met. Descriptive science and art are normative, in the sense of describing what is. Ethics includes the systematized knowledge of what ought to be. It is systematized valuing and emerges from the union of whole science and whole art—"whole" in the balance between their analytic, synthetic, and reduction-to-practice aspects. I define ethics to include the systematized knowledge of what ought to be. To make the definition of ethics complete we must state what else it includes.

We must examine it as "an esthetic process, a succession of problem, solution, and execution," in Coomaraswamy's words.[2] The statement "thus and such ought to or must be done" is partial and only achieves completion when there is added "if this and that are to ensue." The partial statement "Thou shalt not do thus and such" is in itself a noumenal statement, because it is unconnected. When it is completed, *and in the process converted from a commandment to a prescription* (as Haskell points out[3]) much of the confusing opposition between noumenal and phenomenal disappears. The commandments must be completed in order to yield *if . . . then* statements.

As an example, we may take some passages from Dorothy Sayers' *The Mind of the Maker.*[4] She states this process in theological terms. The term "creed," deriving from *credo* ("I believe"), is commonly applied to statements of religious belief and purports to state fact. This is certainly the purpose of the creeds of Christendom. Sayers points out that "they were originally drawn up as defenses against heresy—that is, specifically to safeguard the facts against opinions which were felt to be distortions of facts." They represent injunctions which are partial *if. . .then* statements, as we have pointed out; and she continues:

> Defy the commandments of the natural law, and the race will perish in a few generations; cooperate with them and the race will flourish for ages to come. That is the fact; whether we like it or not, the universe is made that way. This commandment [for He visits the sins of the fathers . . .] is interesting because it specifically puts forward the moral law as the basis of the moral *code; because* God has made the world like this and will not alter it, *therefore* you must not worship your own fantasies, but pay allegiance to the truth.[5]

The language is certainly not that of a political scientist, but the causal relation of *if. . .then* is clearly there.

The partial nature of a commandment may perform an important service of a psychological kind, but as a partial statement its relation to the whole remains vague and thus unconvincing to many modern minds. This is why it is essential for preachers (the *partial* counterparts, in the field of religion, of engineers) to interpret and complete these statements in their sermons. It may be why many sermons sound like essays in sociology, psychology, and political science. This is not the sole function of a sermon, of course. But philosophy, metaphysics, theology, faith, all may contribute to the formulation of answers to these incomplete *if. . .then* statements..

The science of ecology deals with wholes and is permeated by *if. . .then* statements—statements about the interactions of plants and animals among themselves and with the rest of their environment. It is full of statements about positive and negative survival values. These statements escape scientific censure because they complete the ethical formula. Survival is the *then* part of the problem statement. Theology, history, philosophy, also deal with wholes, as do by tradition all the disciplines of the humanities, and in these the *oughts* ring out with varied tones and emphases.

Technologies, such as religion, law, medicine, engineering, clearly display values because technologists are forced in the process of conversion to practice to pose and solve *if. . .then* problems. Thus, for example, they transform the moral pronouncement "Thou shalt build a firm foundation" into "If thou dost not, *then* the bridge will fall down." The prompt, dramatic consequence which is causally tied to the ethical judgment hides the moral and ethical aspect, since the statement is not made in the familiar partial form; but it does contain that aspect. Extending Dorothy Sayers' language to provide a motto for an Engineer's Handbook we can say: "Divine retribution, prompt and severe, is visited on the technological transgressor." The engineer, physician, lawyer, and even many kinds of craftsmen have their functional creeds, but they call them codes.

Every rational action involves choosing that course which is expected to yield desirable results, and the type of results desired depends on the system of values employed. It is necessary to find some way of evaluating—preferably on a numerical scale—every possible course of action to find the most desirable, especially if many exist. It is here that interesting developments with implications for ethics are taking place. Some of these are discussed by the statistician Irwin D. J. Bross in his *Design for Decision.*[6]

Some aspects of a person's intelligence (for example) can be measured numerically, and such measures are used in judging people for employment or for entrance to college. The values people place upon commodities are measured in dollars, as are the market values of less tangible entities such as labor, services, good will, and so on. Market values that are arrived at through the application of cost accounting, time-and-motion studies, customer surveys, etc.[6] are numerical measures of value. Bross also describes other value systems now being experimented with besides the dollar scale.

This field of applied valuation might welcome the man trained broadly in history, classical studies, and ethics who had also mastered some science and mathematics. Since research in this field is bound to continue because, being designed to help technologists to make decisions, it has immense cash value, it would seem profitable for the humanist to enter it, bringing scientist and humanist together in the resulting technology. The humanist can take courage from the showing he has already made in such areas as operations analysis and strategic intelligence during World War II. The concept of a number attached to a value should not be shocking to even the most sensitive academic, since in grading students, teachers make numerical estimates of value.

Values appear at the higher levels of abstraction. In Figure 3 there are no values to be found at the plane of perception. Things just are, and are observed. At the next level, where things are given names, still no values appear. But values may adhere to thc names because of their connections with other constructs. A value has no phenomenal reality except in its recognition. Values may, of course, be projected into things, or constructs, when they actually are in the observer. "What a gorgeous heap" says the teen-ager, enraptured, but the gorgeousness is clearly in him, for his father sees merely a hazardous collection of used parts. When such a projection is done without consciousness of the process all sorts of confusion can result, as has been shown by Hayakawa, Wendell Johnson, Stuart Chase, and, basically, by Korzybski.[7] At the level of theory, law, and universal principles, values cannot be escaped.

Value judgments are dependent on the system relative to which they are made. And as the system is broadened and deepened, the local, relative judgments of a low level of abstraction give way increasingly to more valid, less arbitrary, higher level judgments that point to an extrapolated absolute. Such a transformation in breadth and depth is extraordinarily difficult, as the whole of history shows. The difficulty is reflected in the pain and effort, often in the bloodshed, that have attended these advances—advances represented by the Magna Charta, the Bill of Rights, and the United Nations, to name a few great secular institutions which have embodied value judgments. But the fact that these transformations are conceived and sought is of crucial importance to the culture of the world. (This is why Communist political philosophy, committed to disruption and conflict as it is for the expressed purpose of world domination, is deeply opposed to the United Nations.)

We say that the more whole the system the more securely values inhere. This is based on the premise that any given theory gains in validity as more and more instances are found which support it. In Figure 3, for example, the theory is validated by the large number of connections among constructs. Remembering, however, that appearances can be deceiving and that an internally consistent system can always be achieved by ignoring inconvenient facts which cannot be comprehended by the theory, at least two further demands must be made if we wish to recognize values and ethical principles of the greatest validity. The constructs comprehended by these principles must be of the widest possible qualitative and quantitative variety. Also, there must be the greatest number of connections with the plane of perception. In effect, we demand connections with nature. We must determine to what extent a system of ethics corresponds with the way nature behaves and with the way man can behave. Particularly, since it is fundamental, we must ask to what extent the moral premises of a system are irreducible, resting upon some validating ground that excludes other thinkable sets of premises. That is to say, we must ask whether as premises they support a merely formal system, no better than any other, or whether they are objectively valid.

In one of his books, Professor Collingwood makes passing observation that if the Christian basis for our culture were removed the scientist would no longer have "any motive for doing what inductive thought gives him permission to do. If he goes on doing it at all, that is only because he is blindly following the convention of the professional society to which he belongs."[8] This statement, postulating a connection between scientific activity and the premises of our culture, suggests a means of testing the validity of our system of ethics, of valuing.

The decision to sustain the ideals of scientific objectivity is a moral decision and is continually remade in the context of our Christian culture. This is not fortuitous. Recall the remark of Nietzsche: "Conscientiousness in small things, the self control of the religious man, was a preparatory school of the scientific character, as was also, in a very preeminent sense, that attitude of mind which makes a man take problems seriously, irrespective of what personal advantage he may derive from them."[9] Nietzsche was biased against Christianity, and so his words give added weight to a statement made by J. MacMurray: "Science, in its own field, is the product of Christianity, and its most adequate expression so far, . . . its capacity for cooperative progress, which knows no frontiers of race or nationality or sex, its ability to predict, and its ability to control, are the fullest manifestations of Christianity that Europe has yet seen."[10] And the philosopher Karl Popper, agreeing with this statement, says: "I too believe that our Western civilization owes its rationalism, its faith in the rational unity of man and in the open society, and especially its scientific outlook, to the ancient Socratic and Christian belief in the brotherhood of all men, and in intellectual honesty and responsibility."[11]

In the known diversity of the philosophies of these writers we have made at least a partial test of the validity of the ideas upon which they seem to agree. I can carry the test further, for these statements define in part the liberal tradition. Operating in the real world, the liberal tradition manifests itself in what I would call liberal democracy, and I have in the Russian culture a comparison case against which to test the validity of my argument.

Here, however, we must be careful not to be misled by words. An example will make this clear. A group of American physicists who visited Russia during 1956 reported factually upon their experiences when they returned. An editor of the Baltimore *Sun* directed to Dr. Freeman Dyson, one of the American scientists, the following question:

> It is commonly stated by men of science that freedom is essential to a healthy scientific climate. And yet we learn from members of your group that Russian science, which has surely to put up with security arrangements more stringent than ours, is in a flourishing condition, and that Russian scientists show evidence of the highest morale in their personal and scientific life. How can this be so?[12]

Dr. Dyson's reply leaves no question about political freedom. "This, of course, does not exist in Russia, and will not exist in the foreseeable future," he says.

> But a reasonable scientific freedom does now exist. That is to say, Russian physicists enjoy the basic professional freedoms, to work on problems of their own choosing, to publish their results, and to discuss their ideas with foreign colleagues. These freedoms are restricted by security rules which are similar to ours, perhaps slightly stricter . . .

The editor was not satisfied, for in a discussion of Dr. Dyson's remarks he said that "the paradox of scientific progress in an unfree society still wants an explanation."[13]

Now the explanation of this "paradox" lies in the kind of analysis contained in this book. First we must see that "science" and "freedom" have different meanings in different contexts, and we must qualify them to fit the factual context.

There are certain areas of certain kinds of science wherein the freedoms enumerated by Dr. Dyson may have no relevance to *political* freedom. These are the analystic areas in the *physical* sciences—areas which comprise fact gathering: observing, measuring, analyzing, and recording. All science rests upon these activities. But their pursuit is little influenced by political freedom in the physical sciences, and it was of physics that Dr. Dyson wrote. Physical measurements and chemical observations of all kinds are politically neutral in themselves. In the sciences of biology, psychology, or sociology, analytic activities may not be neutral, and they may be subject to any political restrictions of freedom imposed on the scientist. An ideology such as Marxism, which claims absolute validity, must, to sustain that claim, exclude or distort inconvenient facts. Thus, even at the relatively neutral level of observation or enumeration in data-gathering, we must specify what *activity* of science and what *kind* of science we are talking about.

In analytic physical science, then, the question of the importance of political freedom is not really germane and poses no real paradox. But the editor of the *Sun* inquired about science in general.

Continuing our investigation of this "paradox," we turn to Mr. G. L. Talmon's *The Rise of Totalitarian Democracy*. Distinguishing liberal and totalitarian democracies, he says: "The liberal approach assumes politics to be a matter of trial and error, and regards political systems as pragmatic contrivances of human ingenuity and spontaneity. It also recognizes a variety of levels of personal and collective endeavor, which are altogether outside of the sphere of politics."[14] We recognize in this description our own political system, with its opportunities for trial and error, for mistakes and triumphs; with its checks and balances and tremendous diversity in political and nonpolitical detail. "The totalitarian democratic school, on the other hand," continues Talmon, "is based upon the assumption of a sole and exclusive truth in politics. It may be called political Messianism in the sense that it postulates a preordained, harmonious and perfect scheme of things to which men are irresistibly driven, and at which they are bound to arrive. It widens the scope of politics to embrace the whole of human existence." Here, we recognize Marxism, with its extravagant claims to philosophical certainty and its insistence that all human activity is political. The history of many sciences in Russia shows how the scope of politics is widened to embrace the whole of human existence.

At the interpretive levels of science, the synthetic activities, we see that the larger the area of human knowledge and experience embraced the more the laws of science become touchstones for testing prevailing cultural posits. In a free and open society, should these posits not meet the test, they change—albeit slowly, painfully, and with a skeptical regard for the possible fallibility of the laws themselves. But in the "Messianic" scheme of the Soviets, scientific theory *is* political theory. Thus, at the synthetic level, since political theory is not free, science is not free and cannot thrive if the laws of nature are found to disagree with the Messianic cultural posits of society. The history of mathematics, genetics, physics, psychology, and other sciences *at this level* in Russia bears witness to this view, as do accounts of the rationalizations and sophistries and evasions to which practicing Russian scientists have resorted in the effort to get on with their science and at the same time satisfy the demands of the political censor. Such accounts have appeared in *Science,* the *Bulletin of the Atomic Scientists,* and other journals in recent years. The spectacle would be amusing were it not so tragic, and so dangerous in its effects.

The answer to our "paradox" is that whole science cannot progress freely in an unfree society, but some *parts* of science may appear progressive and healthy, especially when these parts are essentially analytical in nature.

The actual state of affairs is far more complicated than this broad analysis can indicate, yet the core argument is correct.

Some of the complexity is discussed in a report by Ivan D. London, in the *Bulletin of the Atomic Scientists*, dealing primarily with the field of the psychological sciences.[15] He warns that to get an actual picture of Soviet science one has to be careful about interpreting what is written:

> Much that is written and said in the Soviet Union is in the nature of set incantation, protective ritualism, and conformistic camouflage. As an indication of the everyday workings of Soviet science, such material is not to be taken seriously. In the Soviet Union scientists in many areas know very well how to indulge in self-commandeered verbal exercise calculated to impress the Party overseer, before proceeding with the real business at hand.

In other words, the scientists pay lip service to the political requirements. The complexity of the situation is indicated by London's observation that the political requirements have at times produced improvements. Thus, he says, official espousal of the Soviet doctrine relative to Ivan P. Pavlov produced positive effects in psychology and psychiatry which "had been for many years in a sad state." The result was "for the time being, a good one," though the eventual result was to put psychology in a straight jacket. Complicating the issue further is the prestige accorded scientists and the attendant increases in pay and freedom of the spirit for accomplishment. Few situations are ever wholly good or wholly bad.

London's report goes on to say that while much "publicized verbiage" is published for the intellectual public outside of such disciplines as physics, symbolic logic, and information theory, yet "where practice and ideology contend in Soviet science, ideology eventually gives way. Ideology can be manipulated, but not practice; a thermonuclear weapon either explodes or it does not. The tough-minded leadership in the Soviet Union is interested in results, whether garnished or ungarnished with ideological greens."

The conflict between a "Messianic" ideology and the values we see immanent in the highly abstract laws and principles that unite the whole field of true knowledge and experience is not easy to demonstrate outside science. Objective tests are not so easy to apply to music, art, and literature as they are to science. In the field of physics, the political line about "decadent Einsteinian relativity theory" is demolished by the atomic power plants and the particle accelerators which physicists and engineers can build only through the application of Einsteinian relativity. They work. But I suspect that in the fields of music, art, and literature the political cant is not so readily testable. (I speak as a scientist. Perhaps an artist can see the failures of the ideology in art as clearly as I can in science.) But surely if there are connections between the arts and sciences comprising the field of knowledge and experience, we can safely apply to the nonscientific areas the conclusions arrived at in respect to freedom in science. For surely drama, poetry, or novels written to a rigid social theory will lack freedom of design, interpretation, and possibly even expression, even if this lack is difficult to test.

Freedom is essential to a healthy scientific climate because it is requisite to scientific objectivity. This is a function of the entire scientific community and involves free communication of data *and* interpretations, and free criticism and operational testing of them against objective fact. Freedom is essential to—even defined by—a healthy culture. It is an *absolute standard* of what is proper to man. It is one of the components of liberty, another of which is intellectual freedom.

Mark deWolfe Howe, in an eloquent essay on "The Legal Basis for Intellectual Freedom," writes:[16]

> We began our national existence in the conviction that there are some phases of an individual's life which are not only beyond the control of government but beyond its reach as well. The area of a man's unchallenged sovereignty was furnished with what the political philosophers called his unalienable rights, among which, of course, was the pursuit of knowledge.
>
> One aspect of this constitutional presupposition deserves particular emphasis. It was accepted in the 18th

> century, not primarily for the utilitarian purpose of promoting the enterprise of enquiry and thus accelerating the discovery of truth, but for the higher spiritual purpose of securing the individual mind from tyranny. This was among the most important contributions of Christian doctrine to American political theory. What is signified, in so far as Law was concerned, was that the individual scholar and the isolated heretic, rather than the enterprise of scholarship or the pursuit of heresy, became the effective instrument of freedom. Our Constitution and our law make no commitments in favor of academic or scientific freedom as such; their guarantee is that the individual's mind—whether that mind be academically, politically, or scientifically inspired—should be beyond the reach of government.
>
> Our law still looks upon intellectual freedom as a right of individuals and not as an obligation of groups. When government denies the scholar or the scientist the enjoyment of his right, he stands essentially alone against the state. In any such conflict, particularly when the people's fears support that state, the outcome is readily predictable. The individual succumbs.

Howe acknowledges that the mind of man is not entirely beyond the control of government, since society has the power to punish beliefs that it considers to be immediately dangerous. But the methods through which the power of society is exercised are restricted. It is a betrayal of the cause of freedom to tolerate punishment "by processes that history condemns and tradition has outlawed. . . . For our Constitution contains the broader assertion that no person shall be deprived of life, liberty, or property without due process of law. That assertion, I suggest, embodies the basic standard of decency which history has converted into law."

After a survey of certain aspects of current attacks upon intellectual freedom, he continues:

> We will somewhat dissipate the gloom, I believe, and also serve the cause of freedom if we recognize that in-

> tellectual liberty must find its strength beyond the law and through other agencies than those of government. Nearly ten years ago Judge Learned Hand, as he always does, gave us the warning of wisdom. "I often wonder," he said, "whether we do not rest our hopes [for the survival of liberty] too much upon constitutions, upon laws, and upon courts. These are false hopes: believe me, these are false hopes. Liberty lies in the hearts of men and women. When it dies there, no constitution, no laws, no court can save it; no constitution, no law, no court can even do much to help it."
>
> In my judgment no organizations other than universities and churches are strong enough to assert against the state that something larger than the fate of individuals is being destroyed by the abuse of power. It is timidity, not wisdom or statesmanship, that converts all problems of freedom into questions of law. Our Bill of Rights is, of course, a code of law, but it bespeaks convictions that lie beyond the law and will only be preserved as a living commitment when the institutions dedicated to freedom, with courage and fortitude, demand the prerogative of freedom and the right of self-government.

These examples suggest why Christianity sustains science and technology and those arts whose activities are effective in the long run. It is because this religion, in spite of abuses, strongly intensifies the positive, creative, constructive interactions among people, states, and nations. It recognizes and preaches the superiority of cooperation over conflict as a way of life, of disinterestedness in adjudication, of a respect for facts, and of the importance of connecting fact with theory. There is a wholeness about Christian doctrine and practice at its best. The world of nature is not evil but a sacrament. Men have duties toward each other—"love thy neighbor," "judge not"—and the individual is unique and valuable for himself.

Finally, in rejecting the idea of formal truth as the basis for judging an ethical system we must reject cultural relativism, the theory that all cultures are equally valid ("good") and valuable. This is simply mislabeled egalitarianism. It affirms, for example, equal validity for the culture pattern of Dobu, which is so ferociously disintegrative and full of conflict that it is dying out, and that of Hopi, which is so positive and constructive that it is surviving in the most adverse circumstances. Cultural relativism is confusing and disruptive; and, characteristically, says Haskell, it has the backing of the Communist Party, but only with reference to the democracies—the Party does not allow any culture equal validity with the Soviet!

The more whole the system, the more securely values inhere. This insight exposes the error in such a statement as the following one by a contributor to a symposium on *The University and Society*.

> The creative scientists of England are in our universities; the creative poets, dramatists, novelists, artists, musicians, are not. Which is perhaps the reason why scientists talk less of the crisis in the universities than arts men.[17]

A more likely reason that humanists talk more of crisis is that, normally dealing with wholes as analytical scientists do not, the humanists are in a position to see more clearly the division and fragmentation that exists and thus to feel a sense of crisis.

Fragmentation is a product of the unrelieved specialization and increasing complexity in our culture. Complexity is not a property of things but a relationship which the process of abstracting serves to counteract. As Haskell puts it, the greater the power of abstraction, the fewer the things that are complex to the organism in question. The genius is the man who can devise a way of representing simply relations which had previously seemed complex or of stating even in a complex way relations that could not previously be stated at all. The synthetic act which overcomes diversity and complexity, countering the ill effects of unrelieved specialization and attendant fragmentation, the synthetic act which introduces something new, is called an act of genius. Such an act is so difficult that it is not surprising to find the initial product thorny and unfamiliar. The amazing thing is that the act occurs. When, for example, Einstein's theory of relativity was first promulgated, it was understood by few people. But through teaching, interpretation, and familiarity, much of the elementary part of the theory has become available to graduate students and even to some undergraduates. Complexity is modified by the ability to abstract, to determine principles and priorities, and to apply them to abstractions of lower level. No single discipline or area of knowledge has a monopoly on this ability.

Abstraction from parts of systems may yield inadequate concepts. Inadequate concepts yield confusion, uncertainty, and frustration. Such "negative" emotions can also result from division and conflict between scientists and artists. To set into motion the potent creative forces latent in our universities and in our culture and to give point and direction to the insights we have revealed, it is necessary to synthesize the study of parts of systems into the study of whole systems.

In the previous chapter I spoke of the Absolute, which comprises Beauty in esthetics, Perfection in ethics, and Truth in science. Each of these corresponds to the most positive value judgment in its field. Values are emotional judgments too, and the highest values coincide with the most positive, ennobling emotions. Absolutes, values, emotions are parts of a dynamic whole.

Because of the differences between the sciences and the arts, the most lucid scientific statement may be obscure to an artist and the clearest artistic statement vague to a scientist. The only corrective for this situation is for scientists and artists to have enough understanding of the other's fields to become at least amateurs in them. The ideal, I think, is a scientist with the *sensitivity* of an artist, and an artist with the *knowledge* of a scientist. Such a man would be able to interpret and judge the deliverances of his senses, whether or not aided by instruments, in the light of scientific knowledge. He could see the connections between his data, his own experiences and intuitions, and the insights provided by history; and he could thus view himself and his work in the context of his contemporaries and of the past. He could live as a constructively functioning part of the whole system of humanity—past, present, and future.

CHAPTER 9

Reduction to Practice: I

My theme has been that the sciences and arts differ in essentials at the levels of data and emphases but converge at the levels of the laws and great principles which give us pictures of the world. For although the pictures are drawn from different points of view, it is still the same world (we must assume) about which we gain knowledge and experience in these ways. These insights (which are by no means new) may be used to heal the schism which exists between too many artists and scientists, philosophers and technologists, to release the creative powers which mutual respect, understanding, and trust can generate. But first, let us examine the occasions where, as Martin Johnson has said, "both by historical accident and by the misfit of incompatible temperament, the contacts between science and art have brought one or the other to contempt or frustration."[1]

Science Overborne by Art. This section and the following ones will necessarily be incomplete. I can but suggest the outline of ideas and refer the reader to authorities for the fuller structure. Since art and science interact so intimately together to comprise a culture, it is possible to disentangle the effects of one on the other only in those special cases where art and science are developed to different degrees. The lessons these cases may teach us can be applied to modern problems only with the greatest caution. Especially is this true of the following case.

In the lively and provocative group of essays from which I have just quoted, Johnson has investigated some of the areas of "misfit" in contacts between science and art. With a wealth of fascinating detail and documentation he has developed the theme that even in a society where scientists and science are highly regarded, science may stagnate if there is "a lack of balance between logic and imagination." The data that he uses are derived from the study of medieval Oriental history.

Certain astronomical instruments surviving in China from the thirteenth century, he finds, provide testimony that Chinese inventiveness in scientific design and observatory technique had brought the practice of astronomy to an advanced stage long before a similar stage was reached in Persia, the rest of the Moslem world, or Europe. Indeed, Chinese astronomy in some respects anticipated the European by at least four hundred years. Yet in spite of contacts with Moslem and European scientists, Chinese astronomy, through some overriding conservatism, remained stationary "until the impact of a younger and livelier European science caught its frozen dignity in the seventeenth century."[2] Moslem astronomy, with a less lengthy history, perhaps, than the Chinese, suffered the same stagnation. In both cases, Johnson thinks, the cause was a lack of balance between the aesthetic and the scientific components of culture. This was reflected in a scientific conservatism among the Chinese. The result among Moslems was different. In the observatories of Asia, North Africa, and Moorish Spain, where a tremendous amount of elaborate work was done, the advances made were only advances in detail. This was because of a

> crippling blindness with an aesthetic basis—an infatuation with the Ptolemaic cosmography of cycles and epicycles, wherein the motions of the planets, sun, and moon, were described (accurately enough) by a system of earth-centered circles around which other circles rolled.
>
> To a mind reveling in the complex poetic imagery of Arab and Persian art, the aesthetic attraction of the rolling epicycles was an insidious temptation. To have suggested replacing them by ellipses, the one geometrical form capable of uniting a mechanical treatment throughout a solar

> system and thus fulfilling the need that science must be communicable, might have seemed as gross a vandalism as it later seemed a blasphemy to the less esthetically developed European pioneers. So an age in which the arts and sciences lived briefly together was unfruitful, through misreading the terms of independence and interdependence of each partner.[3]

The point of this example is one not often insisted on. It is that, given the appropriate conditions, art can stultify science. This is a warning explicitly given by Johnson and gives a certain perspective to the next section.

Art Overborne by Science. In an earlier chapter I touched on the destructive effect that science can exert on art when it is mistakenly considered to be purely analytic. The physicist-novelist C. P. Snow has pointed out how the imitation of "science" has affected some literature.[4] One response of novelists to the overwhelming success of science, he says, has been "to take refuge in a trivial kind of belles-lettres, made up of snobbery and nostalgia." Another response has been "to jump on the bandwagon of science by using scientific terms, not taking too much care to use them accurately." "But," he says:

> the queerest misappropriation is of the word "experimental" as the name for the novel of a particular subdivision of sensibility.
>
> "Experiment" has a real meaning in inductive thought. Some novels, such as Proust's and perhaps Stendahl's, can be called "experimental" without stretching it too far, but to apply the word to a kind of novel-writing which fundamentally has not budged for thirty-five years, from Dorothy Richardson through Joyce and Virginia Woolf to Carson McCullers, is just nonsense. Let me give some typical examples: *Pointed Roofs* (Dorothy Richardson), *To The Lighthouse* (Virginia Woolf), *Party Going* (Henry Green), *The Heart is a Lonely Hunter* (Carson McCullers) and at the extreme, *Finnegans Wake* (James Joyce).
>
> Whatever we call this variety of novel (moment-by-

moment novel, total-recall novel, have all been suggested), it is by far the most important and characteristic response to the scientific climate. For these novels are an attempt to find a specialization which is some sort of answer to science's specialization. In them the scope of the novel has been narrowed as never before. The questions about men and society that less timid predecessors asked—they have been sacrificed. The reflective mind has been sacrificed. All that is left is an attempt to reproduce the moments of sensation, to convey just what it is like to experience this instant of the here-and-now. Great talent has gone into this attempt, but it appears now as the most hopeless cul-de-sac in the novel's history.

The reason that this attempt has led to a cul-de-sac is that it has been in imitation of analytic science (or in response to analytic science)—in any case, *partial* science. Snow indicates clearly that this is so: the "specialization" has "narrowed the scope"—all that is left is the reporter, the analytic craftsman. "The questions about men and society" are those that deal with wholes. They require synthesis. And, since "the reflective mind has been sacrificed," those questions are no longer asked. E. M. Forster has discussed this sort of approach at some length in *Aspects of the Novel*.[5] He would perhaps distinguish what I have called analytic from synthetic with the phrase "it is talk, talk, never song."

Taking the analytic part for the whole of science is not solely the fault of the humanist. During the early history of any science the analytic work seems to be mistaken for the whole. Each new science which has arisen during the last several hundred years and been considered in this way has necessarily influenced artists of all kinds—sometimes to copy, sometimes to revolt.

Philosophy Overborne by Fragmented Science and Art. In the previous two sections, I have described rather briefly how either art or science may stultify the other. The phenomena clearly are the result of fragmentation of knowledge and experience (reflected in the highly departmentalized university), for when this fragmentation exists it is difficult to see the body of knowledge and experience for the whole that it is. The positive values of Christianity, supported as they are by the sacramental view of the world as a whole, are overborne by an excess of the secular, with its emphasis on separation and distinctions. This fragmentation (encouraged by the Communist doctrine of chaos) creates the climate of meaninglessness and absurdity which many philosophers have generalized into a picture of the universe.

The influences seem actually to have been exerted most strongly via philosophy. I have already quoted the statement of an educational philosopher to illustrate a popular misunderstanding of science: "modern science is no longer merely a report of particular facts." This reflects the intellectual climate we have been describing, and there have been many revolts against such "science" by people who felt the inadequacy of the formulation.

Perhaps such revolts are found in the partial philosophies of phenomenology and early existentialism. These must be called partial as long as they pretend to the name "philosophy." In the overproductive hothouse of phenomenology (which claims through introspection to be able to obtain "eidetic truths" that "have the validity of empirical fact"), there grew a crop of political theory of which the deformed fruit, "thinking with the blood," augured the harvest. Existentialism, "the gravedigger of western European culture,"[6] has at one of its centers conflict and struggle. Spier describes this:

> My neighbor can only feel the urge to destroy my freedom if he is to answer the call to fulfill his own freedom. What we have said applies to everyone, "Thus my neighbor is for me the devil, and life in social relations with others is similar to the fall into sin."[6]

And on Sartre's answer to the question "What is man?" he quotes Zuidema:

> His origin is absurd, his Existence is absurd, and his end is absurd. And the non-absurd of human Existence exists within this relentless horizon of absurdity. The non-absurd

> of human Existence consists of the meaningless ascription of meaning to an unchangeable absurd reality. And this ascription is made by a freedom which chooses itself.

Clearly, there is no universal integrative principle here but largely double talk, meaninglessness.

These "philosophies" contain some truth, of course, but being partial truth it is false or meaningless when extrapolated to the higher level of a philosophy. Dialectical and historical materialism is such a partial truth, based on an analysis by Karl Marx of a local condition and extrapolated to a universal, as Haskell has pointed out.[7] It is the work of a sick man coming to the conclusion that sickness is universal and natural.

There is no point in weighing errors and placing blame except as a warning. Dr. James B. Conant's comment that "my own observations lead me to conclude that as human beings scientific investigators are statistically distributed over the whole spectrum of human folly and wisdom much as other men" sums up the situation if we note that fragmentation is folly, and that it is a mistake to allow the foolishness of some artists or scientists to injure the status of all.

Constructive Influences. There are three constructive aspects of the interactions of artists and scientists that I would like to touch upon: ways in which they have served each other in a professional way as sources of inspiration and subject matter; ways in which they have served and can serve in interpreting each other to the public; and ways in which each makes use of the other's tools.

It is certainly likely that the artist has influenced the scientist and even suggested the direction he should follow, but it might be difficult to give detailed evidence of such an influence. It may well be argued that the experiments of Leonardo da Vinci were those of the scientist who could not be distinguished from the artist in the same man. The imaginative writings of Jules Verne and H. G. Wells might be thought to have suggested directions of research, though they may well have reflected a cultural milieu out of which both art and science took their directions and into which the sensitive writer saw deeper and recognized sooner what was to come. Again, I can only suggest possibilities, and turn to more concrete examples of influences, examples of the arts influenced by science. If I turn to these more concrete cases, it is because they can illustrate my point with more clarity than the others, even if I risk overemphasizing the power of science. But there are two aspects to these matters. If one aspect seems clearer, it does not mean that the other is not important.

As I noted earlier, the mathematicians Lobatchevski, Bolyai, and Gauss, and later Riemann, engineered an "escape from Euclid" when they invented the postulates upon which the two systems of non-Euclidean geometry could be constructed. (There are presently two non-Euclidean geometries. One is built upon the assumption that no line can be drawn through a given point which is parallel to a given line; and the other assumes that two lines can be drawn through a given point parallel to a given line; see Figure 4.) With these examples before them, mathematicians felt themselves free to roam in those fields whose boundaries are set by the rules of logic. Entire systems could be constructed subject only to the restriction that their basic postulates not contradict each other. Mathematics once more became a field to be tilled by the imagination. It could well come to be described as "the oldest of the humanities and the most modern of the sciences."

Naturally, the formal systems devised by these mathematicians could not be expected to reach a nonscientific audience for a considerable period of time. However, by the second half of the nineteenth century there was a great interest among writers, poets, artists, historians, and philosophers in the scientific discoveries of the day. Through this interest, fed by popular lectures given by such great scientists as Herman von Helmholtz and John Tyndall, the new attitude eventually flowed over into the realms of art, poetry, literature, philosophy, and indeed into all of life, being transmuted in the process to meet the needs of artists and scientists. When these new formulations were actually reduced to practice, were brought into the realm of technology, a tremendous infusion of life was experienced. This was, I think, behind the flowering of "experimental" art, music, poetry, writing, architecture. Not that there had been no such experimentation before, but that here was an explicit *modus operandi* for getting fresh or different approaches to any work. An heuristic device had been provided, though it led through misunderstanding to fragmentation.

For example, a painter with the new point of view could say that it is dreadfully Euclidean to look at only one side of an object at a time, as our senses limit us to doing. Since we know the person or object to be three-dimensional, why not paint all sides at once—and maybe even the interior as well? Such changes in postulates in the hands of masters like Picasso have led to fresh and moving art. It was as though shackles had been struck from the imagination, and indeed, many artists looked to science for new knowledge and experience.

Peter Blanc is specific on this point:

> The scientific attitude with which the impressionists approached their art is well known; they themselves did not hesitate to acknowledge their debt to science. Their spokesman, Pissarro, in answer to a letter from de Bellio arguing that scientific research into the nature of color and light, anatomy and the laws of optics, could not help the artist, replied: "Now everything depends on how this knowledge is to be used. But surely it is clear that we could not pursue our studies of light with much assurance if we did not have as a guide the discoveries of Chevreul and other scientists. I would not have distinguished between local color and light if science had not given us the hint; the same holds true for complementary colors, etc." The neoimpressionists, Seurat and Signac, devoted themselves to scientific research, studying Maxwell's experiments, Charles Henry's treatises, the analyses of light and color made by the American scientist N. O. Rood, and Chevreul's color theories. Until he severed his connection with the

> neoimpressionists, Pissarro used to refer to this group as the "scientific impressionists" as opposed to Monet, Renoir and Sisley, whom he scornfully termed the "romantic impressionists." Romantic or not, these painters were scientifically minded, too, for Monet as well as Seurat had studied the optical discoveries of Helmholtz and Chevreul.[9]

But if shackles were struck from the artist's imagination so—because of the climate produced by the philosophies of fragmented knowledge and experience—were the shackles which constrained him to be sane struck off. Previously, an integrated view of nature and man had constrained the artist to act sanely—to act for his survival and the survival of his culture. But the response to the new climate in many artists and humanists was that of a mind going to pieces—matching by a kind of obscene mimicry a world going to pieces. Many people considered this madness to be evidence of honesty, realism. But as I have said before, it takes rationality to discover irrationality, and not the other way around. The ills of the world are not healed by going crazy. To go "beat" is to abdicate the difficult task that should be the artist's: to heal and to enoble.

We could continue this catalog in other areas of the arts. Music underwent tremendous turbulent changes which continue to our own time. Maurice Ravel attempted to use a limited set of tones in his works, which gave them their characteristic quality (but whose possibilities seem to have been exhausted already). Béla Bartok spoke of the need for an utter break with the musical postulates of the nineteenth century. The twelve tones of the musical scale, previously considered in terms of related groups and more or less formal figures, became twelve functionally unrelated tones, and, in the hands of such masters as Schoenberg, Igor Stravinsky, and von Webern produced new sounds seemingly unrelated to music of the past. I have argued the danger of casting loose from connections which support synthesis. These composers avoided chaos through the form of the work—through associated form and through a content of verse or dance to which the music was linked in its performance. New experiments of many kinds continue to be tried in music, sculpture, architecture, and all the other arts.[10]

This outburst of unfamiliar forms has naturally startled people. Also, nonsense and excesses in the name of the new freedom have been legion, particularly in those areas of human activity where empirical tests of soundness are difficult to make. Ironically, in the midst of the ferment, science has provided a conservative force. In science, change for the sake of change has not been common—changes have usually had a rational basis, and tests for validity have generally been available. The motto which represents the operation of the public aspect of scientific objectivity has been "test all things; hold fast to that which is good."

How much these influences that seem to connect scientific theory with art theory rest upon rationalization is difficult to determine. A priori, one must expect some interchange in a society where learning can be freely discussed, but to suggest a connection between Einstein's *Special Theory of Relativity* (1905) and Picasso's first cubist picture (1906-1907) is to rely on numerology. The two movements—one in physical science, the other in painting—may well be "correlative movements in the evolution of the western mind."[11] But although artists and physicists may use the same words (relativity, fourth dimension, space-time continuum, etc.), they do not attach the same constructs to them.

Much clearer evidence of the influence of science and scientists upon the arts is provided by Professor Marjorie Nicolson in her essays on the effects of the telescope and of the microscope on English and Continental literature and poetry.[12] The evidence is clearer perhaps than in the previous example because the influence was more concrete, and we can look back with some perspective.

On the night of January 7, 1610, Galileo looked at the heavens through an improved telescope which he had built. With "incredible delight" the lonely observer saw stars which had never before been seen. He speaks of the "absolute novelty" of his discoveries. As he continued his observations he noted craters and chasms on the surface of the moon; and on the sun, spots, which changed their positions from day to day. His reports over the years, with their wealth of fascinating new information, continued to amaze the world and stirred up tremendous interest in the manufacture of telescopes ("optic tubes") and in amateur astronomy, as the new astronomical knowledge became widely disseminated.

We can only hint at the effect of his reports on literature and poetry. No longer could my mistress's satiny complexion be likened to that of "fayre Diana," for the moon's face had now disclosed crags, craters, and excrescences. Durable classical figures of speech, armament of writers and poets, became outmoded; and poet and artist were on their mettle to invent new figures acceptable in the new scientific climate.

Professor Nicolson writes of the effect on the young Milton (who is thought to have visited Galileo, then an old man, when he journeyed about Italy in 1638):

> As almost in one night Calileo saw a new universe, so Milton, having grown up in a world he had placidly accepted from the past, on some occasion "viewed all things at one view" through a telescope. Like his own Satan.
>
> Before his eyes in sudden view appear
> The secrets of the hoary Deep—a dark
> Illimitable ocean, without bound,
> Without dimension . . .
>
> That experience he never forgot; it is reflected again and again in his mature work; it stimulated him to reading and to thought; and it made Paradise Lost the first modern cosmic poem, in which a drama is played against a background of interstellar space."[13]

When microscopes became widely available a strong effect on science, art, and literature resulted which again demolished many old clichés; and required the scientists, artists, and writers to create new symbols for their ageless themes. This also may be studied through an essay by Professor Nicolson.[14]

While the exciting new discoveries of Galileo did most certainly affect the literature of succeeding generations, as Professor Nicolson has shown, they could not affect his contemporary, Shakespeake. Though both were born in the same year, Galileo outlived Shakespeare by twenty-six years, and his first report on his telescope observations, in his book *Sidereus nuncius* ("Starry Messenger"), came in 1610, at about the time of Shakespeare's retirement, and after he had written most of his plays. Yet there is a connection of another kind between these two great men, for, as the philosopher Charles W. Hendel has noted,[15] both men responded to the tensions and contrasts of the times. The one speaks, for example, through a Hamlet; the other through his Starry Messenger. "Man is like a god, yet he is not a god but, in the face of infinity as a speck of dust," and in the next generation it was Blaise Pascal, mathematician and philosopher, who would say, "the silence of the infinite spaces makes me afraid."

There are many ways in which the scientist and artist can support each other and so influence constructively the public esteem of both. Partly it is a matter of showing reasonable respect for each other's fields, interpreting each other's, and acting upon this respect and interpretation.

Writers who show how science and art depend on each other and supplement each other illustrate through their work one way of raising the dignity of art and science. A number of them have been quoted or referred to in this chapter, and there are many others.[16] I would be the last to suggest that all can be sweetness and light among such different creative temperaments as are found in artists and scientists. But respect can accompany disagreement and will be reflected in the lay reaction. An anti-intellectualism that begins against science will end by swallowing art too if it is not checked at the start. Because the two are connected in the body of knowledge and experience, injury to one is damage to the other.

It is particularly in the enterprise of interpreting science to the layman that the artist can constructively aid the scientist while at the same time securing his own profession. For while ordinary laymen will read literary prose and poetry, will attend concerts, plays, and exhibitions of painting and sculpture, generally they will not turn so easily to scientific writing.

This is an indictment of scientific writing, which often (certainly in the research journals) follows a style that is repellent and dehumanized. The author does not report the prejudices he had to overcome, the fumbling, the mistakes, the false starts that he made, or the accidental discoveries. Everything seems to proceed by an orderly plan from introduction to conclusion. This is dry to the lay reader, especially if he is not familiar with the sparse notations and deliberately colorless jargon that the scientist uses. And it may even seem to him, if he is perceptive, to be somewhat dishonest, for he knows that the human mind is not *that* infallible. In defense of the scientist I must point out that the report is his own work of art. If he does not report the human difficulties along the way (which the editor with limited space would not permit in any case) it is because they would destroy the elegance of the presentation. Even great painters cover up with opaque color the preliminary sketches and trial lines that they make on the unfinished canvas; and autograph manuscripts, with their erasures and fumblings, are usually published only posthumously. The scientist does not write research papers for the layman but for the specialist like himself. Generally, he is too busy to worry about public relations except with his colleagues. This is indeed a naïve, though refreshing attitude. It is often a price paid by the specialist to the demands of his research.

It is unhealthy for the public not to understand the great discoveries, enterprises, and activities of all kinds which affect the course of society. The increasing interest of serious magazines that have no explicit scientific orientation in literary articles about science with sound scientific content is a heartening sign. It implies customer interest. It tends to repair the injury to the public intelligence and to science done by neglected communication. There is room for more of this. We need an atomic Arrowsmith.[17]

Poets traditionally respond to the great forces about them in their own way, as Dr. J. Z. Fullmer has said,[18] and as we showed in an early chapter. The best example that I know of is described in Ann Lodge's psychological interpretation of Milton's Satan.[19] His Satan, she finds, as revealed in "Paradise Lost," is a brilliant study of paranoia. The symptoms of paranoid behavior: "megalomania, the need to dominate, persecution complex utilizing projection and exaggerated self-reference, retrospective falsification, and an absolutely logical, though delusional, character of thought," are sensitively and incisively portrayed by the poet. Satan's four principal sides display, point for point, she shows, the four types of reaction to frustration recognized by psychoanalysts.[20] She concludes that

> Milton's Satan represents what in clinical psychology would be considered a classical case of paranoia, displaying in highly abstract and symbolic form all the essential, characteristic symptoms. Can this be what the character of Satan has always represented to the fantasy life of a large portion of mankind, representing human cognizance of this syndrome for thousands of years, indicating its recurrent and enduring character, and human wisdom in classifying it as Satanic and doomed?[21]

Interpretation of an old theme in a modern idiom may be read in Archibald MacLeish's "Signature for Tempo" (part II):

> These live people
> These more
> Than three dimensional
> By time protracted edgewise into heretofore
> People

Mr. MacLeish's long poem "Einstein" shows "the awareness of the poet to the content of the early versions of the Einstein theories and the kinds of calculations that went into them," says Dr. Fullmer. The poem, published in 1929, reads in part:

> . . . he lies upon his bed
> Exerting on Arcturus and the moon

Forces proportional inversely to
The squares of their remoteness and conceives
The universe.
                    Atomic
                                        He can count
Oceans in atoms and weigh out air
In multiples of one and subdivide
Light to its numbers.

I do not expect art to convey knowledge as its primary function, but it may be bred from knowledge, perhaps, or convey knowledge "in addition." What I mean can be shown in reference to the first five of the lines quoted from "Einstein." This excerpt was given to a group of Freshmen at Yale, and they were asked to interpret it. They had been studying Newton's theories. They all, of course, saw the relation to the formula we presented in Chapter 2, and pointed out how the poet had transformed it to his own uses. But several of them said that this was not really the main point. For, they said, the poet is telling us that Einstein is exerting two forces. One is the weak, indeed vanishingly small, gravitational force which he exerts upon Arcturus and the moon. The other is that tremendous conceptual force with which, lying upon his bed, he "conceives the universe." He creates through this force a new universe. The physical reality of the gravitational force, then, is only a small part of the reality conveyed to us by the poet through the magic of his idiom.

The great poets, writers, and artists of the future *must* be respectable scientists themselves. This is the message I find in Lodge's essay on Milton's Satan, for Milton, great poet that he was, clearly anticipated key concepts of modern psychology. I am certain that literature and art contain many such anticipations. Nowadays, the artist must probe even farther ahead; but it must be on the basis of knowledge of what is now known scientifically. Artistically inclined students must take, rather than evade, science courses. Only if they are cognizant of what science has to offer can they create works which inspire us, instead of revolting us; only by knowing their language can they speak to scientists.

Lastly, the scientist and artist can support each other by acting out their understanding and respect, for actions speak loudly to those who observe them. This is neither difficult to do nor rare in occurrence.

Because of the nature of specialized scientific language and the requirements of a laboratory, it is not common for professional writers, artists, and musicians to be amateur scientists. On the other hand, it is common for scientists to be amateurs in the arts. Without choosing individual examples of scientists, I can point to the exhibits of its members' art works held during occasional meetings of the American Chemical Society. In some comunities of scientists isolated by circumstances, such as those at Oak Ridge and Los Alamos, orchestras, string quartets, drama and painting groups, which produced good works, were organized with mostly scientific personnel.

While it is difficult for a non-scientist to become an amateur in some branches of science, the way is open in many others. There has, for example, been a tremendous increase in interest in astronomy, reminiscent of the popular interest in the seventeenth century. Many fields of botany, zoology, geology are open and are being exploited by amateurs. We can expect a great increase in interest in science as good instruments become cheaper and more plentiful (there is no reason why one has to stop with telescopes). The main thing is that in the process of performing, the amateur comes to *understand* the spirit of his avocation.

In reducing their works to practice, the scientist and the artist use the tools of the other—the scientist uses intuition and the artist uses the empirical approach. Neither scientist nor artist need fear to respect the other, for the creative acts that they perform bear striking resemblance at their inception, however much the final products differ. The actual statements of artists and scientists support this view.

Consider, for example, the statement of the great mathematician, K. F. Gauss: "I have got my result; but I do not know yet how to get it."[22] It states a theme which is echoed in a report about the physicist Lord Kelvin, quoted by Dr. Rosamond E. M. Harding in her *Anatomy of Inspiration*: "Often he had to labour to devise explanations of that which had come to him: and instances are known of his spending whole days upon trying to frame or recover a demonstration of something that had been previously obvious to him." Many scientists and artists state that whole ideas or compositions come to them "all at once" and then have to be laboriously worked out later. Dr. Harding says that "occasionally a piece of music will come complete, or almost so, just as occasionally a poem comes out in its entirety. Schubert's songs often appear to have come straight away. When he had read the Erl-king several times over in quick succession he wrote it down so rapidly 'that the very notes seemed to tumble over one another.' "[23]

I have barely touched one of the many features that seem to appear when artists and scientists speak of their creative efforts. The greatest diversity is shown among these people, but it does not show any particular pattern that distingiushes artists from scientists; they are only people of different kinds. For example, Edgar Allan Poe disclaimed inspiration. "The Raven," he said, was worked out step by step, leaving nothing to accident or intuition. Walt Whitman seems to have been extremely methodical in collecting ideas to fit a particular theme he wished to write upon.[24] Oliver Goldsmith, and Robert Browning occasionally, designed their compositions first in prose, then versified them.[25] This procedure sounds like the procedure of a person carefully designing an experiment to test some hypothesis.

On the other hand, as related above, some workers get their whole inspiration in a flash, or with great speed.[26] "Blake, referring to his poem *Milton* in a letter to Thomas Butts, says, 'I have written this poem from immediate dictation; twelve or sometimes twenty or thirty lines at a time, without premeditation, and even against my will.' " And, Dr. Harding continues,

> George Sand, after describing Chopin's creation as miraculous and coming on his piano suddenly, complete, or singing in his head during a walk; says that afterwards

> "he began the most heart-rending labour I ever saw." It was a series of efforts, of irresolutions, and of frettings to seize again certain details of the theme he had heard; he would shut himself up in his room for whole days, weeping, walking, breaking his pens, repeating and altering a bar a hundred times, and spending six weeks over a single page to write it at last as he had noted it down at the very first.[27]

I do not know of any scientist responding to frustration in quite this way, but I feel certain that a good deal of laboratory glassware has gone the way of Chopin's pens—and for the same cause.

CHAPTER 10

Reduction to Practice: II

Unfortunately, there are too few constructive efforts to bring the arts and sciences into healthful interaction. And because the efforts that are made are isolated, their functioning is not usually recognized as the integrative activity it is; they lose the power that would come with united action. At the same time, the increase in specialization which is occurring without respite continually widens chasms between disciplines. Thus, thc unhealthy state we have recognized tends, by a kind of feedback which operates uncontrolled, to worsen.

The problem is largely one of lack of direction. It is a result of the loss of communication between art and science and the consequent disappearance of that synergistic action of onc upon the other that is needed for a healthy culture. For it is out of the functioning of art and science in a whole, integrated system that those moral and ethical principles arise which can give direction to a people's efforts and sustain their creative drives. The problem must at the same time be met at the level of the individual person.

The hope for healing our cultural lesions lies in education. But it cannot be an education in comfort and adjustment. It must be an education demanding the most strenuous efforts and producing profound emotional and intellectual satisfactions. It must be an education with no terminus and no pat solutions to problems. It must be an education which strongly intensifies the constructive, cooperative, integrative aspects of knowledge and experience, and intensifies their reflections in our deepest feelings of human interdependence. It must, in short, be an education with "mystic qualities" to "enchant, charm, clarify, edify, and nourish" the human spirit.[1]

One foundation for such an education lies in the vision we have evoked of a sphere of knowledge, experience, and activities as a connected and living whole. This is shown schematically in Figure 16. The arts and sciences in their most characteristic expressions lie along the equator of this sphere. Each discipline

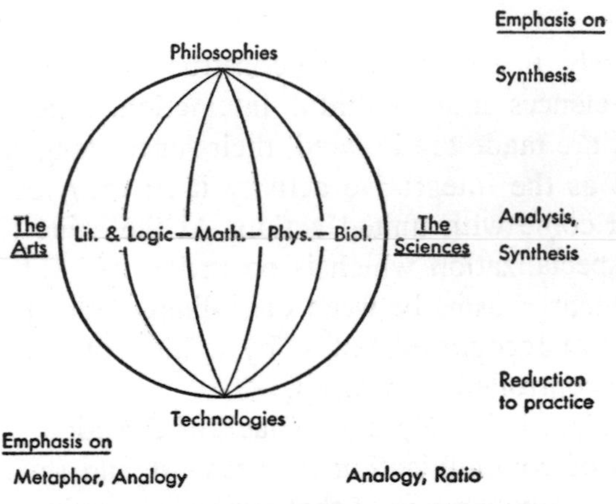

Figure 16. Summary Diagram.

in this area extends its influence toward the poles of philosophies and technologies. Diversity within unity is the theme of this image, for although the disciplines are distinct, yet no tool of communication and no creative intellectual or emotional activity is entirely absent from any part of it. The emphases vary, and from these variations arise those differences among disciplines which, interacting upon each other, can strike off creative sparks. But I must warn again that a figure such as Figure 16 *must not be taken literally*. It simply states in terms of analogy and metaphor one theme of this book.

We saw that in the arts analogy and metaphor—whether discursive or presentational in utterance—are the most common tools of communication. But when some quantitatively very precise similarity must be drawn, the artist may use means verging on ratios. In the sciences, ratio and analogy are the usual tools, but metaphor, though scientifically less common, is invoked e.g. in the "magic numbers" of nuclear physics. Here, too, utterance may take presentational or discursive forms. Again we see that the realms of art and science fuse at their edges and converge at their poles.

Looking next at the activities of analysis, synthesis, and reduction to practice, once more we see evidence of unity in the disciplines. For while the technologies of every discipline emphasize reduction to practice, they continually analyze and question their own activities, endeavoring always to refine their methods. The arts and sciences more nearly balance analysis and synthesis; but in every one of their disciplines, along with these activities flourish tests of validity which rely on reduction to practice. The philosophies emphasize synthesis; but, as in the technologies, the evaluation of the philosophy against experience and the attempt to improve it is continually practiced.

It is clear from this formulation why the integration of the arts and sciences is most commonly achieved in the technologies and philosophies. The latter are by their nature synthetic. In the technologies, the reason for this union is somewhat different. Since arts and sciences grow out of the data of the world (broadly speaking), to return to the realm of phenomena, as the technologies do, is to return to the union at its origin.

The technologist thus unites art and science. His profession forces him to embodiment, which means that he must meet all the exigencies that mark the individual event. For example, when an architect conceives, designs, and builds a structure, art and science meet in his technology. He is vitally concerned with questions of aesthetics. However evanescent his own definition of architectural beauty may be, he nevertheless produces a structure which reflects his own sense of what is true and beautiful. But at the same time, the test of reduction to practice requires that he meet the particular, local problems that arise. He must solve the problem of how to make a sound foundation on that particular spot. He must fit the design to the special use for which the building is intended as well as to the designs of other structures in the area. He must meet all the local requirements of a legal, economic, political, and psychological kind, ensuring as well the mechanical soundness of his work. Analogous examples of other technologists could be given. The physician must similarly consider all the factors that are individual to his patient; the lawyer, to his client. The dramatist must consider and reconcile not only the emotional and intellectual demands of his plot, but the practical demands of his actors and audience —psychological, social, physical demands—and the demands of the stage itself, with its mechanical limitations and its special advantages.

In interpreting this image of the sphere of knowledge, experience, and activities, we find many additional evidences of wholeness.

First, there is the work itself. Any work of art or science, in whatever part of our sphere, which results from an honest attempt to find out and communicate truth, helps to bind the whole together. Communication between persons is necessary to an integrated world, and it is through the work, whether it is a poem, a theory, a composition, or a building, that communication occurs. Some works comprehend smaller areas of truth than others; some provide subtler insights; some speak more clearly. The value of a work is judged by these differences. The work which comprehends more, at whatever level of abstraction, breaking through the limitations of time and space, is greater than that which unites less. But each is part of the whole, and its connections bind the whole. Hence, if each is seen in the light of the whole, it and its context are strengthened.

This does not license either superficiality or excessive specialization. The connections unifying various disciplines become apparent if a given discipline is studied deeply in its analytic, synthetic, and reduction-to-practice aspects at various levels of abstraction. Some of the connections which bind the sphere of knowledge and experience together arise through these activities. Others arise out of the methods of communication, others from the areas of overlap, and still others from the convergence into techniques and philosophies. The operations of these connections cannot be appreciated from a superficial point of view. A narrow specialization, on the other hand, may blind. Either a superficial or an overspecialized work, being in effect unconnected because the connections are obscure, loses its power.

Second, there is the creative act. The poets, physicists, engineers, or philosophers who are able, by whatever magic and effort, to create something which combats the isolation of the individual or lifts up his spirit, which reaffirms the power of the human mind and heart or helps men to extend their comprehension in spite of their finitude—all perform acts of creation. Thus, such acts of creation occur in every discipline and together are a unifying reflection of the quality of the human spirit wherever it may be found.

Third, there is the worker. Human beings differ from each other in an infinite number of ways. The fact has been quantitatively documented by the biochemist-philosopher Roger Williams.[2] His elegant little diagrams (Figure 17) say much that is vital to the humanist. Each man is different, and it follows that each has special abilities in some areas. For some men, these are areas of intellect; for others, of physique; for others, of feeling. Some abilities appear as special mathematical or verbal aptitudes, some as sensitivities to color, tone, or spatial form. Some appear as skill in fine manual work, some as great strength, some as fine coordination or fast response to stimuli. Each ability can be either nourished or starved, and every person has some control over the development of his particular abilities. While some types of ability are more productively used in one kind of work than in another, still, classification of men by their aptitudes beyond the most general categories may be undesirable. It might tend to much more division than is necessary and remove the opportunity for fresh interactions. People are more complex and more capable of the unpredictable in the face of challenge than such classifications usually assume.

It is not the materials of their work that should distinguish

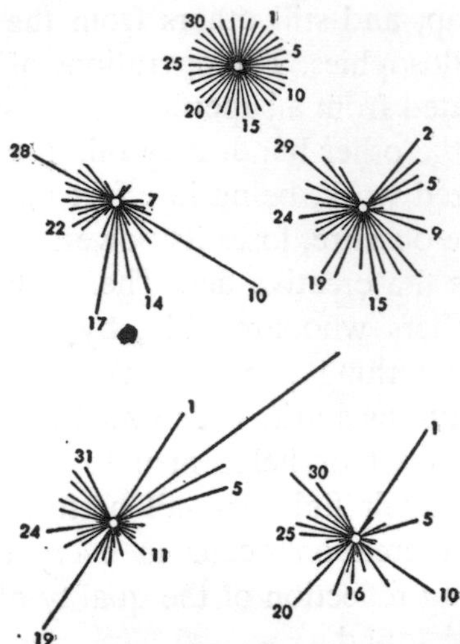

Figure 17. The patterns of four different individuals are shown, with an "average," the symmetrical pattern. (Plotted by Professor Roger J. Williams, *Free and Unequal,* University of Texas Press, 1953, pp. 107, 110.) The successive numbered lines represent the items: 1-5, taste sensitivities for creatinine, sugar, potassium chloride, sodium chloride, hydrochloric acid; 6-17, salivary constituents: uric acid, glucose, leucine, valine, citrulline, alanine, lysine, taurine, glycine, serine, glutamic acid, aspartic acid; 18-31, urinary constituents: citrate, unknown base, unknown acid, gonadotropic hormone, pH, pigment/creatinine ratio, chloride/creatinine ratio; hippuric/creatinine ratio, creatinine, taurine, glycine, serine, citrulline, alanine. The lengths of the lines indicate values relative to the average, which is adjusted on a scale to give the symmetrical pattern shown at the top.

men but the quality of their devotion to their callings. The manual laborer who gives his best is as good and truly a *man* as the creative artist or scientist who gives his best. Both are superior, in terms of human worth and integrity, to the intellectual or physical featherbedder. Work well done, of whatever constructive kind, unites the scientist, humanist, technologist, and philosopher. If we recognize this old wisdom we may strengthen the foundations of our education.

Truth in one part of this sphere is connected to truth in any other part. A truth may be symbolized by a small *t*. Then we can imagine our field of knowledge and experience as a nexus of connected truths, each partial, in the sense that it is local, but each gaining validity through its connections to others. Truths are not contradictory, only partial; and a truth of one area, such as science, cannot threaten that of another, such as art or religion.

Suppose we diagram this in a simple way:

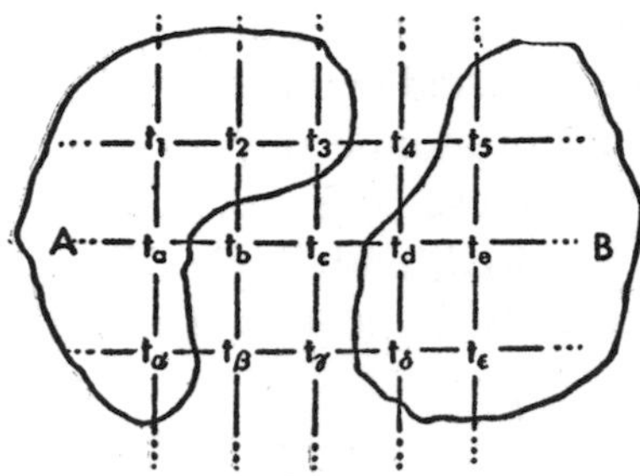

A person **A,** comprehending only the truths looped together, might well adhere to opinions which conflict with those of a person **B,** since both lack the connecting truths lying outside their knowledge and experience. The rational solution of such conflicts is difficult if the connections are not known (e.g. t_4 or t_b and t_c, or t_β and t_γ); but the concept of our field counsels us to believe that the connections can be found and to withhold judgment, defending ourselves, if necessary, with arms, while we search for them.

There always will be erroneous opinions held in the conviction that they are true. The resolution of conflict is as difficult as the correction of error. In some areas of our sphere, like the physical sciences, the criteria for validating a truth (a small *t* truth) are fairly well established. In those areas, it might not be too difficult to correct an erroneous belief, provided the error lies in the public domain—that is to say, provided the error is susceptible of empirical test. In other areas of our sphere, truths (little *t* truths) may be more difficult to validate. The "truth-to" of art may be more difficult to test than the "truth-about" of science. Yet all gain strength through interconnections.

These truths are not immutable or absolute. No one of them necessarily remains unchanged. Indeed, because of the connections, a new insight, which brings the truths of one area more finely into correspondence with perceptions and experience, may alter significantly the truths of another area. This is understandable and reasonable. For the field of knowledge and experience continually expands as new truths appear and take their place in the tapestry. New discoveries in the psychology and physics of vision, for example, affected painting and sculpture. New discoveries in the realms of atomic physics and chemistry changed the interpretation of those sciences without invalidating the truths of Newton, Maxwell, and Boyle. The older partial truths simply found themselves in a new context of newer partial truths.

The figure I have drawn is presented as a kind of visual scaffolding on which to display my argument. I do not mean that all the *t*'s are equally valid or come in packets of the same size. The *t*'s of science are publicly available; those of many of the arts are private and are validated in the private experiences of the communicants, being not necessarily identical to any two persons. But they are all connected in the ways I have described. Similar schemes could be set up for other concepts than truth—for knowledge, meaning, reality and so on—all, of course, in terms of a nexus of small *k*'s, small *m*'s, small *r*'s, and so forth.

These truths are not unmixed with error (small *e*'s). This follows from the fact that, as I said, they are not immutable. It follows also from the general principle that this world being constituted as it is, no absolutes can be obtained. Everything that is communicated or experienced comes to us in terms of truth *and* error, reality *and* unreality, meaning *and* meaninglessness, beauty *and* ugliness, good *and* evil. Still, we are at liberty to extrapolate from these small *t* truths to Truth, in a kind of summation. But such extrapolations require theories.

Finally, if we see the sphere of knowledge and experience as a whole, we recognize that in principle there are no barriers between the parts. Of course we know that in practice barriers do exist, since we are finite creatures—finite temporally, spatially, mentally. The great aim of research in all areas of our sphere is to remove these barriers.

There has been enough success in this direction to encourage us, although not enough to convince us that the goal is attainable. Man's life span has been lengthened, and the onset of mental decrepitude has been delayed. There is some indication that methods of learning and teaching can be improved. Machines to store, process, and recall vast amounts of information are placing increasingly more information at our command. Men are working on new syntheses, at higher levels of abstraction, which comprehend and focus large areas of the field, areas which now must be apprehended piecemeal.[3]

These advances are inevitable and may not be easily grasped. The sphere of knowledge and experience is continually expanding and thereby generating more problems. As we obtain more subtle insights and rise to higher levels of abstraction to comprehend them, the difficulties also increase in subtlety. Therefore, we must not expect that we shall ever reach a state where effort can be relaxed. The unending development of special abilities, techniques, and data for synthesis is the price we pay for life.

We should teach our young people the content of the sphere of knowledge and experience in the continual presence of the connections, emphasizing the *whole*. We should make clear to them the sequence of *if . . . then,* since it encourages a sense of responsibility and gives direction to studies. We should avoid invidious comparisons between disciplines, and should emphasize instead the *quality of the work itself* and the suitability of the tools used in executing it—whether it be a poem, a work of scientific research, a theme, a musical composition, or whatever. In this way we may stimulate personal integrity and help to combat false concepts of status. The studies of young people should be balanced between the arts and sciences, at least in the early period of their education, although an intelligent imbalance should be possible for students who show special ability for intense, creative effort in one direction. As a student proceeds with his education, he eventually must specialize to some degree. The earlier training I have described can keep this specialization in perspective. It is frequently observed that the intense effort required for productive work in a specialty is most easily made by young adults. Having established his education on a broad base a student can in later years broaden his interests as much as he will.

Students who are shown the connections between disciplines and the bases for these connections are better able to see the relevance of their own studies to the whole and to gain a sense of direction in their academic lives. They feel that what they do matters, not only academically but in all aspects of their lives. They can recognize interdependence as healthy, because it is coupled with responsibility and vision, and can accept it as a source of human strength. In such educational directions lie the means for combating cultural anarchy and fission. But if we are to provide these educational directions, we must make certain changes in our overcompartmentalized universities. We need specialists in synthesis, perhaps constituting a university council or seminar, which can attract the services of the most widely cultured staff from all departments. This could function to provide communication to and from departments, and to teach synthetic methods and theory to suitably prepared students.

CHAPTER 11

Retrospect and Prospect

There was a time, it is said, when an intelligent scholar could exhaust the knowledge of his day. If this was ever true, it is no longer. Connected with that earlier time is a picture of a way of life that drew together integrally the arts, sciences, and technologies in a "discipline of intimacy" related to the concept of vocation—a concept that "the artist is not a special kind of man, but every man is a special kind of artist."[1] That union of arts, sciences, and technologies contained the seeds of many of our present difficulties along with the vast increase in knowledge and experience which resulted. Those seeds, slowly germinating, produced pressures which gradually split apart that union, pressures which revealed themselves in, for example, Galileo's science and Descartes' and Locke's philosophies, which cleaved spiritual from physical nature, opposed mind and body, and in their analytical emphasis marked a change "from aesthetic harmonies to mathematical formulae; from contemplative enjoyment to active manipulation and control; from rest to change; from eternal objects to temporal sequence."[2] And these changes, occurring largely within a framework of either/or—that is, demanding a choice between alternatives—led to the loss of that happy interplay among all areas of knowledge and experience which characterized pre-Renaissance intellectual life. A return to that pattern is not now possible. The fruit of knowledge that we have tasted has changed and enlarged our view. To progress we need to operate at a higher level of knowledge and experience. Let us look once more, then, at the problem and try to see where the solutions should be sought.

The source of many of our present troubles, broadly speaking, is the success of analytic science. Although partial, it has been so successful in so many ways that it has piped the tune for philosophers and poets, artists and other humanists, to dance to. Analysis by itself—descriptive, cataloguing through ever finer distinctions—is purely divisive; and the dance it has inspired is a dance of chaotic collisions. The differences in emphasis among science, art, and technology have been accentuated; and their universal scope, their meeting ground, has been obscured. The resulting conflict is active everywhere in our modern world. *Men are divided by what they do, not by how they do it.* Art seems almost to fear an intellectual component, meaning, or use. Science is too often suspect when it exalts the spirit. Specialists must stick to their specialty, so that they can be classified for budgeting. Goods are valued above men, who have degenerated into mere consumers. Technique is value above inspiration, with the consequences predicted by Lord Dunsany: "If the notion spreads, we shall have diamond cutters valuing their tools more highly than the diamonds, with the result that, as long as they cut them in accordance with the rules of the craft, they will cease to care whether they cut diamonds or glass, and then they will cease to know."[3]

What we have witnessed is science in its early stage—analytic, descriptive, *partial* science—influencing philosophy, art, and technology with partial truth and supporting a trend toward increasing, unrelieved complexity which, if it continues, can only terminate in cultural fission. But complexities at the analytic level can be simplified in theories, laws, and philosophies. And provided that these have maintained touch with their empirical sources, they can provide solutions to daily problems. It is at the level of laws, theories, and philosophies that the dangers of cultural fission—the results of the divisive forces—must be faced and removed. In imitating analytic science, the arts have been false both to the humanities and to science—false to the humanities by abandoning their traditional concern with wholes; false to science by picturing a part of science as the whole. This falsity has been recognized by many scholars who have seen how the arts have been led by such imitation into sterile places. Unfortunately, science has been blamed for the sins of the imitators of partial science. This onus can be removed only through understanding that the analytic part of science, though essential, is only one part.

The arts and sciences are supplementary and complementary ways of giving intelligibility to phenomena. In both we find acts that can be classified as analytic, synthetic, and reduction-to-practice. Any mature discipline in either area combines all three of these activities. Moreover, the function of each activity is so different from that of each other activity that they may not fruitfully be identified; when *disciplines* are being compared—for example, for purposes of transferring methods from one to the other—the comparison must be made *in terms of similar activities.*

Science and art are among the great expressions of men's quest for truth. Each gives expression in its own idiom to truths that are discovered through its own techniques. The expressions and idioms are different, and, while in principle anything whatsoever may be a subject for the artist or the scientist, in practice the two tend to deal with different areas of knowledge and experience. These areas are determined by how successfully the techniques of a discipline deal with them, and there is overlapping between the areas.

My central theme has been that the sciences, the arts, the technologies, and the philosophies compose complementary and mutually supplementary ways of gaining and organizing knowledge and experience. In developing this central theme I have worked from the following principles.

There is no single, permanent, complete, universally applicable solution to any complex problem. There are, however, optimal solutions. To be optimal, they must contain enough flexibility to allow for experimentation, development of new solutions, and correction of mistakes. The entire realm of knowledge and experience is a dynamic complex which is continually assimilating new inventions, discoveries, and creations out of men's lives, and discarding those that are useless or outworn.

Men, the active creators of this complex, are themselves influenced by it. Men are driven to seek the unfolding of their powers. But this drive opposes a kind of inertia, so that continued effort is required to maintain the dynamic state (which defines a live culture), and continued wisdom is required to prevent either decay to a static state of death, or explosion into an anarchic, disordered state.[4]

The increasing complexity in any given area of knowledge, experience, technology, or philosophy which operates to hinder the activities of men (because their finitude limits their capacity at any given level of activity) can be surmounted by a process of generalizing and of moving to a higher level of abstraction. Complexities become subsumed in this way under more general concepts. This process is one of the components of progress. It occurs in both the sciences and the arts, illustrating the principle that *neither has a monopoly on any type of activity of which men are capable*. Sciences, relying in large part upon empirically based, cognitive activities, could not survive without the intuitions with which scientists continually surprise themselves; and the arts, inspired by the subjective and intuitive, also rely heavily upon the empirical. Both include technological and philosophical aspects; both are rational enterprises.

The dazzling complexities men have produced and then subsumed under general concepts lead me to the principle that *no limit whatsoever may be put to the possibilities that can be materialized through men's inspiration, will, integrity, and intelligence*. As a further principle I hold that *when the arts, sciences, technologies, and philosophies are brought together in a whole functioning system there emerge ethical imperatives which confirm and extend the noblest ideals mankind has collected and treasured*.

As a corollary to the above principles, we are fully justified in extrapolating to absolutes, which function as conceptual touchstones against which to measure actual accomplishments. Such absolutes are also subject to the generalizing activity which, ideally, arrives at the Absolute, which comprises Beauty from the point of view of aesthetics; Perfection, from that of ethics; and Truth, from that of the theory of knowledge.

I have said a good deal about absolutes. When I use the term absolute, I mean a concept or construct, in the sense defined in Chapter 3, which represents the ultimate, the limit of some theory. In the intellectual enterprise based upon that theory, the absolute becomes a reference point against which actual achievements may be measured. It gives meaning to such measurements and tests, and it receives meaning from them. In the processes of its use, the absolute is embodied in suitable symbols. In the realms of philosophy and theology, absolutes which function at lower levels of abstraction are superseded finally by the concept of the Absolute.

Every attribute, quality, or property is relative in the sense that although it can be judged and given meaning in arbitrary terms, only when it is referred to its appropriate absolute(s) is the arbitrariness minimized. Any quality or property of a relative nature may be analyzed into components such that (in the simple case of two components) the individual manifestations of the quality or property can be placed at some position on an imagined scale, running from one component alone through combinations of the components to the other component alone. If the property can be measured, then the scale can be given a numerical range. For example, returning to the temperature scale discussed in Chapter 7, the scale is quantified from absolute cold (absolute zero) to absolute hot at the other end of the scale. Mundane properties which can be measured are generally found clustered at one part of the scale, and we could calculate, from enough measurements, a norm, or mean for the property within a given range, which could be used as a base point.

Absolute zero, as I said, is an extrapolated limit obtained by mathematical calculation from the results of actual experiments.

The experimental efforts required to get closer to absolute zero become progressively greater the closer one gets, and for metaphysical reasons one concludes that the "point" absolute zero can never be reached. It is possible also to imagine higher and higher temperatures and to calculate an absolute at the hot end of the scale. Again, the closer one gets to the limit, the more difficult are the experiments. Mundane temperatures cluster about a mean and, in general, involve differences from the mean which are small compared with the differences between absolute zero and the temperature of the hottest star. But because we can depart in both directions from the mean, in a manner describable by theory, and because we can formulate a theory mathematically, we feel that we can *postulate* an absolute zero—an infinity of cold—and even give it a number as a mathematical limit (though the number is not "really" that corresponding to the limit but is only as close as makes no difference to the experimenter). This illustrates the important principle that *to determine a mean, or norm, requires only a method of measurement (and patience), while to determine an absolute requires a theory as well. That is, to determine a mean, analysis suffices. To determine an absolute, analysis and synthesis are necessary.*

Some systems of thought use a mean or norm as a reference point; others use an absolute. The two approaches are different. It seems to me more adequate to the demands of the mind—especially in the realm of values—to estimate value from some even dimly seen concept of an absolute than from a mean. A judgment based on a mean might equate a genius with an imbecile as "equally abnormal."[5] But from the point of view of an absolute they would be poles apart.

One can either take a revealed Absolute as a fixed beacon in the light of which all matters whatsoever are interpreted, or one can move through the operations of analysis and the applications of theories to extrapolated absolutes, whose beams, so to speak, may be focused in the Absolute. Each method validates the other through areas of mutual agreement. When I say that out of the proper functioning of the sciences and the arts together there arise ethical and moral imperatives that confirm the noblest ideals mankind has collected and treasured, I am making use of the latter method.

The use of an absolute as a base of reference leaves room for improvement of the mean, while the mean by itself as a point of reference is blind to this possibility. This distinction is important because in this world continual effort is needed to combat degenerative forces (including both disruptive, anarchic forces and petrifying resistances) that ultimately lead to the death of the individual. Individual freedom—indeed life itself—can be maintained only as the result of continual efforts to preserve it. If the mean or the norm is taken as the reference point, we might easily fail to see that there are two different directions for deviation, and we might let the gains that mankind has passed on to us slip away. *We could nevertheless always remain "adjusted"—which means "degenerating."*

But with an absolute as touchstone, the divine discontent that characterizes the human animal is more likely to be recognized and maintained. And even if it is true, as some philosophers and physicians maintain,[6] that man's nature normally drives him to integrate his whole personality, thus presumably working against the degenerative forces I mentioned and automatically improving the norm, an absolute can still perform an important function as a beacon, a star, a goal, as well as a touchstone.

The works, inventions, dreams, and aspirations of men are so wonderfully varied and so potent of unpredictable growth that no single portion of the field of knowledge and experience such as science or art can comprehend them all. For although we cannot deny to scientist or artist any portion of the world of experience and knowledge, each has found certain areas of this world more amenable than others to his tools of investigation, understanding, and communication. Science and art are different. As criteria for distinguishing them we may use the areas of their success, their methods of investigation, their works, and so forth. But in the process of making distinctions, we must aim at the goal of mutual understanding between artist and scientist.

In physical science, where quantitative statements of high precision and wide applicability are common, and where even the narrowest relationship of the most local significance can usually be cast into mathematical form, *ratio* is the chief tool for communication. Every equation is essentially a ratio. But when the data are not convertible to quantitative terms, or when their convertibility is not evident, then *analogy,* the handmaid of research, must be called upon as a means of communication. All sciences and arts make use of analogies when resemblance between relations can be seen but cannot be quantified. I see no clear reason for judging either better than the other. Each bears its own advantages.

However, there are many kinds of knowledge and experience which, though clear enough to the artist or scientist, cannot be communicated even by analogy. They may be subtle and complicated relationships verging upon the ineffable. For these the swift *metaphor* must be used. *The demands of communication may give metaphor a validity in its own sphere equal to that of analogy and ratio in theirs.* All perform similar functions appropriate to the need. While science always moves in the direction of ratio, there seems to be no preferred direction in the arts. Fittingness rules in both.

In the physical sciences, truths, facts, and relationships are easily and well organized through the agency of ratios and other mathematical tools. Such organization is somewhat less successful in those sciences that deal with living beings. In the arts, such organization is a difficult activity, fraught with uncertainties and dangers.[7] It is not that the truths of art are more difficult to come by or more subtle or more complex. But in the arts, partly because of their preoccupation with the subjective, there seem to be more independent variables than in the sciences. These have not yet yielded to the kinds of classifying and measuring tools successfully used in science. In both there are subtleties and richness and variety sufficient to satisfy the most demanding intelligence and the most sensitive feeling. *But there is no reason why the arts must conform to canons devised for the sciences.* Here, too, some recognition of inherent differences forms part of our solution.

The scientific revolution is an authentically new movement in the world. What is new about it is the application of quantitative thinking to whatever will yield to this approach. It has been partially successful and has brought us new truths we never knew and would not have guessed without it.[8] It has also introduced errors and division in our culture we might not have fallen prey to without it. Now we must restore the wholeness to knowledge and experience—to life.

Vigorous moves are being made in this direction, which are responses to the needs of the human spirit.[9] These responses can come only from people who do not fear science, but understand its power and its limitations—people who have such faith in the power of truth, wherever it may be found, that they are not afraid to look for it; people who believe that what is true in art remains true always, but may have to be reinterpreted for a new generation, just as what is true in science remains true always, though it may be reinterpreted and subsumed under more general truths; people whose faith in truth can sustain them in that difficult, creative enterprise wherein the gifts of intuitions are weighed by reason and treated with a sense of responsibility to both reason and intuition.

If humanists understood science and would effectively make their voices heard they could, with the aid of scientists, control the forces of cultural change in the process of their actual generation, directing them in the ways that lead toward the morally and ethically just ends that arise from a union of art and science. This union, when it is a union of whole science and whole art, supports and illuminates anew a noble image of man.

Notes

Chapter 1

1. Report of the Harvard Committee: *General Education in a Free Society* (Harvard University Press, 1945), p. 50. The report states further that science has done more than this; that "it has directly fostered the spiritual values of humanism." But the tenor of the report indicates to me that throughout science is considered as mainly analytic in the sense used in this book.

2. H. Butterfield, *The Origins of Modern Science: 1300-1800* (Macmillan, 1953), p. viii.

3. This is a theme found running through a great many publications of the last half generation. Among these may be mentioned: Sir Walter Moberly, *The Crisis in The University* (SCM Press, 1949); C. P. Snow, *The Two Cultures and the Scientific Revolution* (The Rede Lecture) (Cambridge University Press, 1959), and his essay "Britain's Two Cultures" in the Sunday *Times,* February-March, 1957; Sir Eric Ashby, *Technology and the Academics: An Essay on Universities and the Scientific Revolution* (Macmillan, 1959). See also Chapter 2, note 23.

Chapter 2

1. *General Announcements of the Rice Institute,* Houston, Texas, 1952, p. 133: "As one of the most modern of sciences and, at the same time, one of the most ancient of the humanities, mathematics is regarded as an integral part of any general education." I am indebted for this reference to Dr. Isaac Dvoretzky.

2. Francis Thompson, "The Mistress of Vision." *Complete Poetical Works of Francis Thompson* (The Modern Library), p. 184.

3. For an elementary exposition of Newton's Law, see Gerald Holton, *Introduction to Concepts and Theories in Physical Science* (Addison-Wesley Press, 1952), Chap. 11; R. F. Humphreys and R. Beringer, *First*

Principles of Atomic Physics (Harper and Brothers, 1950), Chap. 5.

4. Julien Benda, *The Great Betrayal,* trans. Richard Aldington (Geo. Routledge and Sons, 1928), p. 64.

5. The term is used by W. M. Urban in *Beyond Realism and Idealism* (George Allen and Unwin, 1949), p. 191.

6. Howard Lee Nostrand, in the Introduction of José Ortega y Gasset, *Mission of the University* (Princeton University Press, 1944), p. 17n, says that Professor Joseph Cohen has termed history and criticism the interpretive humanities, which he distinguishes from the creative humanities.

7. Bertrand Russell, *Human Knowledge: Its Scope and Limits* (Simon and Schuster, 1948), p. 154.

8. John Hospers, *Meaning and Truth in the Arts* (University of North Carolina Press, 1946), p. 235.

9. Personal communication of Herbert H. Harned, Professor of Physical Chemistry, Yale University.

10. Susanne K. Langer, *Philosophy in a New Key: A Study of the Symbolism of Reason, Rite and Art* (Harvard University Press, 1942), 1951.

11. W. R. Matthews, in *What I Believe, by Fourteen Modern Thinkers* (Frederick Muller, Ltd., 1937), p. 5.

12. Cassius J. Keyser, *Mathematics as a Culture Clue* (Scripta Mathematica, 1947), pp. 16-17.

13. S. I. Hayakawa, *Language in Action* (Harcourt, Brace, 1943); Wendell Johnson, *People in Quandaries: the Semantics of Personal Adjustment* (Harper and Brothers, 1946); Stuart Chase, *The Tyranny of Words* (Harcourt, Brace, 1938); C. K. Ogden and I. A. Richards, *The Meaning of Meaning* (Harcourt, Brace, 1923); Alfred Korzybski, *Science and Sanity: an Introduction to Non-Aristotelian Systems and General Semantics* (2nd ed., Science Press, 1941).

14. Hospers, pp. 139 ff.

15. *Ibid.,* pp. 162 ff. The quotation is from page 167.

16. *Ibid.,* p. 173.

17. *Ibid.,* p. 175.

18. This book is an example of synthesis in the last of these categories: a theory of theories.

19. Joseph J. Schwab, "Dialectical Means versus Dogmatic Extremes in Relation to Liberal Education," *Harvard Educational Review, 21,* 37 (1951).

20. Agnes E. Meyer, *Education for a New Morality* (Macmillan, 1957), p. xi.

21. Hospers, p. 75.

22. T. S. Eliot, *Collected Poems 1909-1935* (Harcourt, Brace, 1936).

23. Many of the ideas in this chapter have appeared already as short essays in the literature: Harold G. Cassidy, "Chemistry, Chemical Engineering and Culture," *Journal of Chemical Education, 32,* 86 (1955); "The Engineer: a Blend of Scientist, Humanist, Technologist," *Yale Scientific Magazine, 30,* 4 (1956); and "The Problem of the Sciences and the Humanities: a Diagnosis and a Prescription" (Sigma Xi National Lecture), *American Scientist, 48,* 383 (1960). I am indebted to the copyright owners for permission to use quotations and illustrations.

Chapter 3

1. A. Lowinger, in *The Methodology of Pierre Duhem* (Columbia University Press, 1941), p. 18, says that Pierre Duhem defined positivism in this way.

2. Ordway Tead, "Has Higher Education Any Unifying Principles?" *Harvard Educational Review, 20,* 245 (1950).

3. Harry S. Hall, "Scientists and Politicians," *Bulletin of the Atomic Scientists, 12,* 46 (1956).

4. Editorial in *Science, 123,* 1059 (1956).

5. Henry Margenau, *The Nature of Physical Reality: A Philosophy of Modern Physics* (McGraw-Hill, 1950). Professor Margenau cannot be held responsible in any way for such errors as I may have made in treating his complex and subtle ideas in this abbreviated and simplified form. He has kindly permitted me to use some of his diagrams.

6. A fascinating exposition is given by Herman von Helmholtz, "On the Origin and Significance of Geometrical Axioms," *The World of Mathematics,* ed. J. R. Newman (Simon and Schuster), 1956), I, 647.

7. W. C. Dampier, *A History of Science* (3rd ed., Cambridge University Press, 1942), Chap. 9.

8. H. G. and L. R. Lieber, *The Education of T. C. Mits* (W. W. Norton, 1942); also their *Non-Euclidean Geometry; or Three Moons in Mathesis* (Academy Press, 1931); and their *The Einstein Theory of Relativity* (Farrar and Rinehart, 1945). See also note 6, above.

9. Margenau, pp. 102-103.

10. Ananda K. Coomaraswamy, *Christian and Oriental Philosophy of Art* (Dover Publications, 1956), p. 79.

11. John Hospers, *Meaning and Truth in the Arts* (University of North Carolina Press, 1946), p. 204.

12. *Ibid.,* p. 238.

13. Suggested by Edward F. Haskell, Chairman, Council for Unified Research and Education, Inc.

14. T. E. Hulme, quoted by Hospers, p. 179. In a note on p. 190 Hulme is further quoted: "Between nature and ourselves, even between ourselves and our own consciousness, there is a veil, a veil that is dense with

the ordinary man, transparent for the artist and poet." And, speaking of painting: "The artist dives into the inner flux, and comes back with a new shape which he endeavors to fix. He has not created it, he has *discovered* it, for *once expressed we recognize it as true*. His vision then becomes everybody's." Whether an act of creation is involved is discussed in the text.

15. Margenau, p. 72.

16. F. H. Bradley, quoted by R. G. Collingwood in *The Idea of History* (Oxford University Press, 1946), p. 137.

17. Henri Focillon, *The Life of Forms in Art* (Wittenborn, Schultz, 1948), pp. 10-11.

18. Arnold J. Toynbee, *A Study of History,* abridgement of volumes I-VI by D. C. Somervell (Oxford University Press, 1947).

19. Collingwood in *The Idea of History,* cf. note 16.

20. Margenau, p. 297.

21. Since knowledge is not in question, what is conveyed by different works "not being propositions, do not contradict each other. Some of them are more valuable than others, and some are more imaginatively fruitful; but if there is one which does not seem to 'hold water' in our experience, another may be presented to us to supplant it; it does not invalidate the first, it simply replaces it. As a rule, however, when we have once had a 'prehension' of spatial depth, our perception of it in another painter does not eradicate the first one from our perception, but merely conditions it, or combines with it in such a way as to form a new whole which then influences our further perceptions. Our vision will be colored by both of them acting together" (Hospers, pp. 203-204).

22. In this the humanist pits himself against those barriers that isolate persons. Here is Clive Bell, in a passage from his *Art:* "Men and women who have been thrilled by the pure esthetic significance of a work of art go away into the outer world in a state of excitement and exaltation which makes them more sensitive to all that is going forward about them. . . . It is because art adds something new to our emotional experience, something that comes not from human life but from pure form, that it stirs us so deeply and so mysteriously. But that, for many, art not only adds something new, but seems to transmute and enrich the old, is certain . . ." (quoted by Hospers, p. 191).

Chapter 4

1. Jacques Hadamard, *The Psychology of Invention in the Mathematical Field* (Princeton University Press, 1945), p. 17.

2. *Ibid.,* p. 14.

3. *Ibid.,* p. 16.

4. Harold G. Cassidy, "Electron Exchange Polymers," *Journal of the*

American Chemical Society, 71, 402 (1949).

5. J. J. Becher, *Physica Subterranea,* 1669.

6. Henri Focillon, *Life of Forms in Art* (Wittenborn, Schultz, 1948), p. 9.

7. *Ibid.,* p. 6.

8. *Hyperion. A Facsimile of Keats's Autograph Manuscript with a Transliteration of the Fall of Hyperion. A Dream,* with introduction and notes by Ernest de Selincourt (Oxford University Press, 1905).

9. Quoted by I. B. Cohen, *Science Servant of Man* (Little, Brown, 1948), p. 109.

10. William E. Hocking, *Science and the Idea of God* (University of North Carolina Press, 1944), pp. 107 ff.

11. Reed Whittemore, *The Self-Made Man and Other Poems* (Macmillan, 1959), p. 62. I am indebted to Professor Richard E. Powell for telling me of this poem.

12. Ernest Newman, "Beethoven: The Last Phase," *The Atlantic,* March 1953, p. 70; see pp. 71-72.

13. James B. Conant, *Science and Common Sense* (Yale University Press, 1951), p. 44, says: "The stumbling way in which even the ablest of scientists in every generation have had to fight through thickets of erroneous observations, misleading generalizations, inadequate formulations, and unconscious prejudice is rarely appreciated by those who obtain their scienific knowledge from textbooks. It is largely neglected by those expounders of the alleged scientific method who are fascinated by thc logical rather than the psychological aspects of experimental investigations."

14. Professor Joel H. Hildebrand kindly allowed me to read his notes and permitted this restatement.

15. W. P. D. Wightman, *The Growth of Scientific Ideas* (Yale University Press, 1951), p. 94, says, "it is never wise to deny to men of genius the use of any methods to which their intuition may guide them; they can usually be relied upon to do the right thing, though through the unfamiliarity of the procedure they may give the wrong reasons for doing so!" See also Hadamard's thorough documentation of these ideas; also Gerald Holton, "On the Duality and Growth of Physical Science," *American Scientist, 41,* 89 (1953); and E. Bright Wilson, Jr., *An Introduction to Scientific Research* (McGraw-Hill, 1952).

16. See Philipp Frank, "The Place of Logic and Metaphysics in the Advancement of Modern Science," *Philosophy of Science, 15,* 275 (1948), p. 286.

17. Personal communication.

18. José Ortega y Gasset, *Toward a Philosophy of History* (W. W. Norton, 1941), pp. 231-232.

19. Henri Poincaré, *The Foundations of Science,* trans. George Halsted (The Science Press, 1913), p. 128.

Chapter 5

1. José Ortega y Gasset, *The Dehumanization of Art. And Notes on the Novel,* trans. Helene Weyl (Princeton University Press, 1948), p. 46.
2. Bertrand Russell, quoted in *Journal of Chemical Education, 11,* 493 (1934).
3. Sir Arthur Eddington, *The Philosophy of Physical Science* (Macmillan, 1939).
4. See, for example, Karl R. Popper, *The Open Society and Its Enemies* (2nd ed., Routledge and Kegan Paul, 1952), II, 238.
5. Personal communication.
6. Miguel de Unamuno, *Essays and Soliloquies,* trans. J. E. Crawford Flitch (Knopf, 1925).
7. Ortega y Gasset, *Dehumanization of Art,* p. 67.
8. Unamuno, pp. 55 and 59.
9. The phrase is from T. H. Campbell, "Sermon of the Week," *New Haven Register,* June 6, 1948.
10. The quotation is from William H. Chapin, *Second Year College Chemistry* (2nd ed., John Wiley and Sons, 1926), p. iii.
11. The subject is thoroughly discussed by Henry Margenau, *The Nature of Physical Reality: A Philosophy of Modern Physics* (McGraw-Hill, 1950).
12. Bertrand Russell, *Human Knowledge: Its Scope and Limits* (Simon and Schuster, 1948), p. xi.
13. José Ortega y Gasset, *The Modern Theme,* trans. James Clough (W. W. Norton, 1933), pp. 135 ff.
14. Melvin H. Marx, ed., *Psychological Theory. Contemporary Readings* (Macmillan, 1951).
15. William Ellis, *The Idea of the Soul* (Geo. Allen and Unwin, 1940), p. 33.
16. David Daiches, *Poetry and the Modern World* (University of Chicago Press, 1940); see especially Chapter 4.
17. T. R. Henn, *The Apple and the Spectroscope* (Methuen, 1951), pp. 140-141.
18. William L. Laurence, *New York Times,* April 28, 1940, p. 15.
19. Henn, Chap. 5.
20. F. S. C. Northrop, *The Meeting of East and West: An Enquiry Concerning World Understanding* (Macmillan, 1946).
21. John Dewey, *Art as Experience* (Minton, Balch, 1934), p. 73.
22. *Loc. cit.*
23. I owe this quotation to William Mansfield Clark, *Industrial and Engineering Chemistry, 28,* 620 (1936), p. 623.

Chapter 6

1. George Sarton, *A History of Science: Ancient Science Through the Golden Age of Greece* (Harvard University Press, 1952).

2. Jay Hambidge, *Dynamic Symmetry: The Greek Vase* (Yale University Press, 1920). I am indebted to Professor A. R. Patton for calling this work to my attention.

3. Ruth Benedict, *Patterns of Culture* [New American Library, 1948 (Houghton Mifflin, 1934)], p. 55.

4. Hans Reichenbach, *The Rise of Scientific Philosophy* (University of California Press, 1951), p. 37.

5. Irwin Edman, "The Challenge of the Arts to Philosophy," *Journal of Philosophy, 44,* 407 (1947), p. 412.

6. Personal communication of Edward F. Haskell.

7. Ananda K. Coomaraswamy, *Christian and Oriental Philosophy of Art* (Dover Publications, 1956), pp. 70-71.

8. See, for example, Edmund Fuller, *Man in Modern Fiction* (Random House, 1958).

9. For illumination, see L. S. Kubie, "Some Unsolved Problems of the Scientific Career," *American Scientist 42,* 112 (1954), and W. S. Beck, *Modern Science and the Nature of Life* (Harcourt, Brace, 1958), excerpted in *Saturday Review,* August 2, 1958, pp. 36-37. I suspect that the freedom of the artist in classical times was of a special kind: one is not free to disobey the law of gravitation; one may "dissent" or "defy"—and take the consequences, which are Nature's punishment. One is also free to align himself with the universal law and reap the benefit in terms defined by the canon.

10. Howard Mumford Jones says ". . . the discovery of the irrational has been made possible by reason itself" ["The Creative Intelligence—The World of Ideas," *Harvard Educational Review, 22,* 203 (1952), pp. 209-210].

11. Max Born, *Experiment and Theory in Physics* (Cambridge University Press, 1944).

12. Samuel Johnson, *Rasselas, Prince of Abyssinia* (Cassell, 1899). The essay was written in 1759.

13. Quoted by José Ortega y Gasset in *Dehumanization of Arts; and Notes on the Novel,* trans. Helene Weyl (Princeton University Press, 1948), p. 63.

Chapter 7

1. Henri Poincaré, *The Foundations of Science,* trans. George Halsted (The Science Press, 1913), p. 106.

2. Henri Focillon, *The Life of Forms in Art* (Wittenborn, Schultz, 1948), p. 7.

3. Dorothy M. Emmett, *The Nature of Metaphysical Thinking* (Macmillan, 1946), p. 102.

4. C. F. von Weizsäcker, *The History of Nature* (University of Chicago Press, 1949), p. 176.

5. Sir Arthur Eddington, *The Philosophy of Physical Science* (Cambridge University Press, 1939), p. 123.

6. Support for this view may be found in Ernst Cassirer, *Substance and Function,* trans. W. C. and M. C. Swabey [Dover Publications, 1953 (Open Court, 1923)] and in his *The Problem of Knowledge,* trans. W. H. Woglom and C. W. Hendel (Yale University Press, 1950). An interesting possible illustration of the importance of employing function rather than form in extending reasoning by analogy is to be found in W. P. D. Wightman, *The Growth of Scientific Ideas* (Yale University Press, 1951), pp. 461-462.

7. Ananda K. Coomaraswamy, *The Transformation of Nature in Art,* (Harvard University Press, 1934).

Chapter 8

1. Peter A. Carmichael, "Is it Ethics?," *Bulletin of the American Association of University Professors, 37,* 41 (1951).

2. Ananda K. Coomaraswamy, *The Transformation of Nature in Art* (Harvard University Press, 1934), pp. 64-65.

3. Personal communication of Edward F. Haskell.

4. Dorothy L. Sayers, *The Mind of the Maker* (Harcourt, Brace, 1941), p. xii.

5. *Ibid.,* p. 12.

6. Irwin D. J. Bross, *Design for Decision* (Macmillan, 1953).

7. See Chap. 2, n. 13.

8. R. G. Collingwood, *The Idea of History* (Oxford University Press, 1946), pp. 254 ff. The quotation is from pages 255-256.

9. Friedrich Nietzsche, *The Will to Power,* quoted by Lancelot Hogben in *The Nature of Living Matter* (Kegan Paul, Trench, Trubner, 1930), p. 245.

10. J. MacMurray, *The Clue to History* (SCM Press, 1938), p. 86; see also p. 192.

11. Karl R. Popper, *The Open Society* (2nd ed., Routledge and Kegan Paul, 1952) II, 243-244.

12. Freeman Dyson, "Science and Freedom," *Science, 124,* 432 (1956).

13. Editorial, "Research and Freedom," *Science, 124,* 427 (1956).

14. J. L. Talmon, *The Rise of Totalitarian Democracy* (Beacon Press, 1952), pp. 1-2.

15. Ivan D. London, "Toward a Realistic Appraisal of Soviet Science." *Bulletin of the Atomic Scientists, 13,* 169 (1957). The quotations are

from pp. 169, 171, 173. See also Philip H. Abelson (ed.), "Science in the U. S. S. R.," *Science, 126,* 1095 (1957); and Gregory Razran, "Soviet Psychology Since 1950," *Science, 126,* 1100 (1957). That scientific objectivity *can* operate in the Soviet Union is indicated by "On 'The New Cell Theory,' " by L. N. Zhinkin and V. P. Mikhailov, reprinted in *Science, 128,* 182 (1958).

16. Mark deWolf Howe, "The Legal Basis for Intellectual Freedom," *The Scientific Monthly, 78,* 135 (1954). The several quotations that follow are from pages 135-136, 137, 138.

17. P. M. S. Blackett, "Training for the Professions," *The Listener, 43,* 603 (1950), p. 604.

Chapter 9

1. Martin Johnson, *Art and Scientific Thought: Historical Studies Towards a Modern Revision of Their Antagonism* (Columbia University Press, 1949), p. 21.

2. *Ibid.,* p. 88.

3. *Ibid.,* p. 102. It is interesting to note that G. T. Lodge and associates (in an article in "Introduction to Unified Science," ed. Edward F. Haskell, presently in manuscript form) have shown that leading scientists are extremely strong in both control (intellect) and affect (emotion).

4. C. P. Snow, "Storytellers for the Atomic Age," *New York Times Book Review,* January 30, 1955.

5. E. M. Forster, *Aspects of the Novel* (Harcourt, Brace), 1927.

6. J. M. Spier, *Christianity and Existentialism,* trans. D. H. Freeman (The Presbyterian and Reformed Publishing Co., 1953), pp. 66 and 74.

7. Personal communication of Edward F. Haskell.

8. James B. Conant, *On Understanding Science: an Historical Approach* [New American Library, 1951 (Yale University Press, 1947)].

9. Peter Blanc, "The Artist and the Atom," *Magazine of Art, 44,* 145 (1951), pp. 146-147.

10. Some of the new experiments in music: *electronic music,* composed by putting together pieces of tape upon which have been recorded electronically manufactured sounds as well as naturally produced ones; *musique concrète,* which in somewhat the same way utilizes mostly natural sounds.

11. Paul M. Laporte, "Cubism and Science," *The Journal of Aesthetics and Art Criticism, 7,* 243 (1948-1949).

12. Marjorie Nicolson, "The Telescope and Imagination." *Modern Philology, 32,* 233 (1935); "The 'New Astronomy' and English Literary Imagination," *Studies in Philology, 32,* 428 (1935); "Milton and the Telescope," *ELH, A Journal of English Literary History, 2,* 1 (1935); "A World in the Moon. A Study of the Changing Attitude Toward the Moon in the Seventeenth and Eighteenth Centuries," *Smith College*

Studies in Modern Languages, 17, No. 2 (1936); "The Microscope and English Imagination," *ibid., 16,* No. 4 (1935). I am indebted to Professor James C. Haden for bringing these essays to my attention.

13. Nicholson, "Milton," p. 3.

14. Nicolson, "The Microscope."

15. Charles W. Hendel, in his Yale Alumni Seminar Lecture, June 10, 1958.

16. Douglas Bush, *Science and English Poetry: a Historical Sketch, 1590-1950* (Oxford University Press, 1950); Johnson; Nicholson; Norman Holmes Pearson, in *The American Writer and the European Tradition,* eds. Margaret Denny and W. H. Gilman (University of Minnesota Press, 1950), pp. 154-167; Hyatt Howe Waggoner, *The Heels of Elohim: Science and Values in Modern American Poetry* (University of Oklahoma Press, 1950).

17. There are candidates for this position. One of them, not as well-known as it should be, is *Lance,* by Edward F. Haskell (John Day, 1941). The novels of C. P. Snow are excellent candidates.

18. J. Z. Fullmer, "Contemporary Science and the Poets," *Science, 119,* 855 (1954). The quotations are from pages 857 and 859.

19. Ann Lodge, "Satan's Symbolic Syndrome: a Psychological Interpretation of Milton's Satan," *Psychoanalytic Review, 43,* 411 (1956).

20. N. Maier, *Frustration: The Study of Behavior Without a Goal;* see Lodge, p. 422.

21. Lodge, p. 422.

22. Karl R. Popper, *The Open Society* (2nd ed., Routledge and Kegan Paul, 1952), II, 16.

23. Rosamond E. M. Harding, *An Anatomy of Inspiration* (W. Heffer and Sons, 1940).

24. *Ibid.,* p. 61.

25. *Ibid.,* pp. 62-63.

26. *Ibid.,* p. 14.

27. *Ibid.,* pp. 17-18.

Chapter 10

1. Henry A. Murray, "A Mythology for Grownups," *Saturday Review,* January 23, 1960, p. 10.

2. Roger J. Williams, *Free and Unequal, The Biological Basis of Individual Liberty* (University of Texas Press, 1953).

3. Edward F. Haskell, ed., "Introduction to Unified Science."

Chapter 11

1. Ananda K. Coomaraswamy, *The Transformation of Nature in Art* (Harvard University Press, 1934), p. 64.

2. John Dewey, *The Quest for Certainty: A Study of the Relation of Knowledge and Action* (Minton, Balch, 1929), pp. 94-95.

3. Stephen E. Fitzgerald, "Literature by Slide Rule," *Saturday Review,* February 14, 1953, p. 15. The quotation is from page 54. A terrifying example of just this has been given by Dr. Bruno Bettelheim in *Harper's Magazine, November* 1960, p. 49. He describes the behavior of a German physician at the Auschwitz death camp who observed all correct medical precautions during a childbirth, with the greatest technical care, but half an hour later sent mother and infant to the gas chambers and crematorium.

4. The living system, whether an individual organism, a colony, a nation, or the world of nations, can be analyzed in cybernetic terms as a system capable of adjusting itself to environmental changes, within limits, and groping toward solutions of its problems. The mechanism by which an effect of some action returns information to control the factors that produce the effect—and so modify the behavior of the system—is feedback. This may operate either to control the system and make it adjust itself, as the governor of an engine does, or as a thermostat controls an oil burner, so as to maintain the temperature of a house within a narrow range; or it may aggravate the effect and cause the system, instead of governing itself, to run wild. This latter situation would result if the thermostat were so connected that when the house became warmer more heat was called for instead of less.

An excellently written, thoughtful study of cybernetics, requiring no knowledge of mathematics, is Pierre de Latil's *Thinking by Machine* (Houghton Mifflin, 1957).

5. Howard Mumford Jones, "The Creative Intelligence—The World of Ideas," *Harvard Educational Review, 22,* 203 (1952). See especially page 207, where he traces the change in the theory of genius. Up to the Christian era, genius was considered to be divinely inspired and, until the eighteenth century, a gift of God—that is, the invasion of mortality by divinity. But then the Socratic *daimon* was withdrawn from the genius, leaving only the abnormality. See also Ananda K. Coomaraswamy, *Christian and Oriental Philosophy of Art* (Dover Publications, 1956), particularly the essay beginning on page 89.

6. Eric Fromm, *Man For Himself: An Inquiry into the Psychology of Ethics* (Rinehart, 1947); see, e.g., Chapter 4.

7. The story is told that "the devil and a friend of his were walking along the street, when, some distance away, they saw a man stoop down, pick something up and put it in his pocket. The friend said to the devil, 'What did that man pick up?' 'He picked up a piece of Truth,' said the devil. 'That is bad business for you, then,' said his friend. 'Oh not at all,' the devil replied. 'I am going to let him organize it' " [Raynor

C. Johnson, in *The Imprisoned Splendour* (Harper and Brothers, 1953), pp. 31-32, quotes this passage from Carlo Suares, *Krishnamurti*].

Professor Paul Mus has suggested to me that in the Oriental fable the man who picked up the fragment of Truth had found a sign that a new view of the world would have to be developed, because prevailing Truth, being whole, would leave no fragments lying around. But whatever its original meaning, this parable recalls to us an important difference between art and science. Truth may be organized with greater assurance in the sciences—especially the physical sciences—than in the arts. This property of science has its own dangers, however, for it is too easy a step from recognizing how well Einstein's theories of relativity, say, organize vast reaches of physical truths to (boldly) postulating an absolute quality to these theories and then (arrogantly) forgetting that this was merely a postulate. This danger to science is caused not by science but by scientists who—being naïve, or being incautiously carried away by enthusiasm or a feeling of power, or for whatever complicated reason—lose that intellectual balance which comes from the interplay of art, science, technology, and philosophy.

8. I refer here to such really new knowledge as that of nuclear fission and the synthesis of elements; of chemotherapeutic principles which lead not only to the curing of somatic diseases but to aiding the cure of psychic ones [for references, see S. S. Kety (ed.), "The Pharmacology of Psychomimetic and Psychotherapeutic Drugs," *Annals of the New York Academy of Sciences, 66,* Article 3 (1957), 417-840]; of the detailed physiology of the human brain, which is leading to the location of sites connected to subtle functions; of the kind of logic which is leading to machines that will translate from one language into another [for references see, for example, J. Ornstein, "Mechanical Translation: New Challenge to Communication," *Science, 122,* 745 (1955)].

9. Edward F. Haskell (ed.), "Introduction to Unified Science."

Index